*STARFLEET GUIDES*

**Volume I**

REVISED EDITION

Written by: W. Paul Hollingsworth
Illustrated by: Eve Burge

ISBN: 1–886810–02–8

First Edition, First Printing: June 1994
First Edition, Second Printing: October 1994
Revised Edition, First Printing: October 1996

# STARFLEET COMMAND

Director of Education
San Francisco, Earth

A MESSAGE FROM THE DIRECTOR OF EDUCATION, STARFLEET COMMAND

Welcome to Starfleet Academy. You have either been accepted as a Midshipman in the Academy's Basic Program and are just starting your Starfleet career, or you may be an experienced officer on starship duty returning for training in one of the Advanced Colleges. In either case, your acceptance here is due to your recognized abilities and accomplishments which have elevated you above your peers.

To the Midshipman who has left the civilian life behind for the adventures of Starfleet duty, I envy you. At the threshold of a new way of living, with all of the rich experiences and successes yet to come, your time at Starfleet Academy will provide you an opportunity to form relationships with fellow classmates and seasoned officers which will last a lifetime. Your studies here in Starfleet Academy's Basic Program will not be easy, but with dedication and perseverance, you will leave Starfleet Academy in four years ready to take your rightful place among the elite graduates who have enriched Starfleet ranks and contributed so much to the United Federation of Planets and its members.

If you are a Starfleet officer who is returning for additional study in one of the Advanced Colleges, your responsibilities are two fold. On the one hand, you will be engaged in supplementing your Fleet experience with specialized knowledge which will return dividends not only to you, but to Starfleet, your ship, and your fellow crew members. In addition, you are expected to share the experiences and knowledge you have gained through active service with those just being introduced to this special and exciting life style we have chosen. You will be a basic part of their acclimation. I strongly encourage you to actively seek out and mentor a Midshipman. In this way you will contribute to the camaraderie and esprit de corps which are basic to the success and reputation of Starfleet.

On a final note to all Academy students, I would like to remind you that learning does not stop or start here. It is a continual process. No time spent learning is ever wasted.

Live long and prosper,

Rear Admiral Sharanan
Starfleet Command

# TABLE OF CONTENTS

# GENERAL INFORMATION

## HISTORY

Starfleet Academy was authorized by Article 52, Paragraph 4, of the Articles of Federation, signed in 2161. As stated, the purpose of the Academy was to train "officers and personnel for Starfleet duty." Shortly after the Babel Conference completed its work, an Educational Sub–committee of the Military Staff Committee was established to locate a site for the Academy, complete designs for the campus and buildings, develop a curriculum, and recommend suitable faculty and staff members.

In the meantime, an interim program was instituted to provide personnel to crew the 11 authorized cruisers and their various support facilities until the Academy became operational. Graduates of established universities and other volunteers were screened and sent to a temporary location for transitional training. This six–month "boot camp" trained prospective officers and enlisted personnel to function within the parameters of para–military organization.

In 2165 the Educational Subcommittee completed its work. Its recommendations to the Military Staff Committee and the Federation Council included locating Starfleet Academy in San Francisco (Earth) in close proximity to Starfleet Headquarters. An academic program modeled after the traditional Federation university would produce a graduate with a Bachelor of Science degree in Military Operations ready in all respects for Starfleet duty. After careful review and minor changes, the plan was approved by the Federation Council in 2166.

Construction began immediately. The San Francisco campus was completed in 2168 and began accepting students that same year. The initial program remained relatively unchanged until 2180, when Starfleet Command issued its famous White Paper: *The Future Fleet: A Blueprint for the 23rd Century*.

This report laid out the goals of Starfleet as an instrument of exploration, research, and defense. Although increased exploration and research were the central themes of the report, the specter of another interstellar war like the Earth/Romulan War was an ever–present influence. As additional planets joined the United Federation of Planets, increased security concerns also assumed greater importance. Among the goals included in the White Paper was a greatly enlarged Fleet by the year 2200.

A larger Fleet would severely impact Starfleet Academy's ability to supply sufficient graduates to man the new ships and bases envisioned. The Directorate of Education, Starfleet Command, began its own investigation of how the Academy could respond to the projections contained in the White Paper. The Directorate's final report, entitled *Educational Paradigms for the Future Fleet*, was released in 2181 and submitted to the Federation Council for approval.

This report addressed not only the impact of the White Paper on Starfleet Academy, but also laid out an expansion program which would include advanced degrees at the Master of Science (MS) and Doctor of Philosophy (PhD) levels. The primary conclusion of the report was that the current Academy in San Francisco had inadequate facilities to absorb an increase in the numbers of students. Two alternates were offered: move Starfleet Academy to another location and enlarging the campus to accommodate more students; or build additional Academy campuses in other locations. Increasing the number of Starfleet Academy campuses was Starfleet's preferred solution.

The ramifications of these alternatives were hotly debated in the Federation Council. Earth, as a founding member of the United Federation of Planets, wielded great influence in the Council and pushed to retain the Academy on Earth. Several other planets, recognizing the advantages of having their own Academy campus, formed a caucus to lobby for the establishment of more than one campus. The acrimonious debate lasted over a year, preventing Starfleet Command from taking any action.

Finally, the decision was made to retain Starfleet Academy on Earth, but move the campus to another, more spacious locality. A study was immediately begun to identify suitable locations. Following a full Earth year of investigation, the search narrowed the choices to four cities: Albuquerque, Houston, Kinderfield, and Wollongong.

The situation was dramatically changed by the Great California Quake of 2183, which completely destroyed Starfleet Academy in San Francisco as well as the majority of Starfleet Headquarters facilities. One aftermath of the confusion which followed was a reversal of the Federation Council's decision to maintain only one Starfleet Academy campus.

As finally instituted, the plan for additional academies included a campus for Home Fleet (Quadrant 0) on Treasure Island in San Francisco Bay, one for First Fleet (Quadrant 1) on the planet LoriLynn, one for Second Fleet (Quadrant 2) on the planet New Britain, Starfleet Academy Third Fleet (Quadrant 3) on the planet Enya, and Starfleet Academy Fourth Fleet (Quadrant 4) on Avatar.

Construction of Starfleet Academy (Home Fleet) began in 2184 and was completed in 2186. In the meantime, plans were drawn up for the additional four academies and submitted to the Federation Council and the affected planets' governments for approval.

Approval for Starfleet Academy (First Fleet) came in 2185. Starfleet's Corps of Engineers began construction in the same year and the first students arrived in 2187. Both Starfleet Academy Second Fleet and Third Fleet were completed in 2188 after two–and–a–half years of construction. Avatar, in Quadrant 4, expressed numerous objections to the plans for Starfleet Academy (Fourth Fleet), which delayed its opening until 2190.

The following time line is provided for easy reference:

2161 United Federation of planets established.

2162 Educational Sub–committee of the Military Staff Committee begins development of Starfleet Academy.

2165 Initial report from the Educational Subcommittee submitted to the Federation Council for approval.

2166 Initial report approved by the Federation Council.
Construction of Starfleet Academy begins.

2168 Starfleet Academy in San Francisco, Earth, completed and accepts first students.

2180 Starfleet Command's White Paper published.

2181 Directorate of Education publishes its follow–on report to the White Paper.

2182 Decision is made by the Federation Council to retain Starfleet Academy on Earth but in larger facilities.

2183 Great California Quake destroys Starfleet Academy and most of Starfleet Headquarters.

2184 Construction begins on Starfleet Academy (Home Fleet).

2185 Construction of Starfleet Academy (First Fleet) begins.

2186 Starfleet Academy (Home Fleet) completed and accepts first students. Construction of Starfleet Academy (Second Fleet) and Starfleet Academy (Third Fleet) begins.

2187 Starfleet Academy (First Fleet) completed and accepts first students.

2188 Plans for Starfleet Academy (Fourth Fleet) finally approved by Avatar and construction begins.
Starfleet Academy (Second Fleet and Third Fleet) completed and accepts first students.

2190 Starfleet Academy (Fourth Fleet) completed and accepts first students.

Each Academy is, of course, an integral part of Starfleet Academy, and provides the same high level of education to its students. Procedures, academic schedules, curriculum, and courses are identical on each campus. The location of an Academy in close proximity to Fleet operating areas has reduced overall expenditures per student while allowing each Fleet Academy to develop its own personality drawn from the unique tactical and historical situation existing in that Quadrant. The concept has proven to be an unqualified success.

# ORGANIZATION

As shown in the accompanying chart, the Commandant of each Academy reports directly to the Director of Education, Starfleet Command. The Director is, in turn, responsible to Starfleet Command, which is subordinate to the Military Affairs Committee of the Federation Council. Although authorized wide latitude in day–to–day Academy operations, the Commandant must obtain prior approval from the Director in any instance which may have an effect on educational policies or procedures beyond the confines of the specific campus.

At the Academy level, the faculty and staff of each College report to the Dean of that College. Deans are responsible directly to the Commandant, as are the Commanding Officer of the training vessel and the Academy's administrative staff.

Starfleet Academy is divided into two main divisions: Basic Training (which is part of the College of Fleet Operations) and Advanced Colleges. Basic Training provides the Midshipman a comprehensive basic education in preparation for further educational experiences, and an introduction into Starfleet life. Completion of the program results in a Bachelor of Science Degree in a specific field (Engineering, Life Sciences,

Medicine, Physical Sciences, Social Sciences, or Space Sciences) and the brevet rank of Ensign, Starfleet.

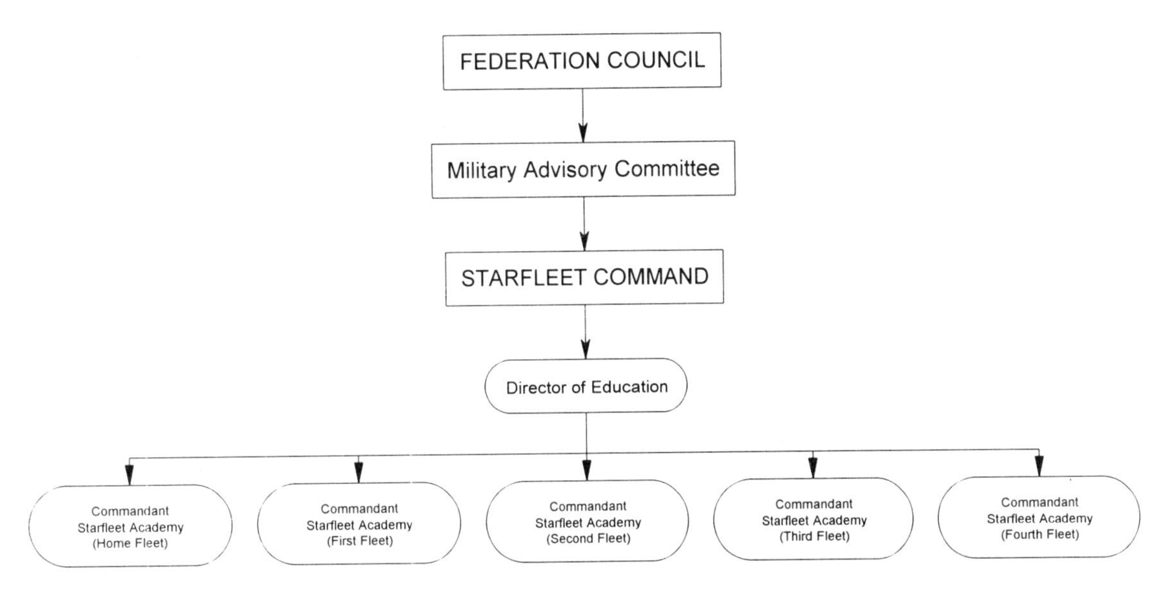


Starfleet Education Organization Chart

In some special cases, the graduate will be offered the opportunity to continue as a student in one of the Advanced Colleges.

The Advanced Colleges, composed of seven separate, specialized curricula, offer a Master of Science (MS) or a Doctor of Philosophy (PhD) in certain fields: engineering, Fleet operations, life sciences, medicine, physical sciences, social sciences, and space sciences. Generally, students in the Advanced Colleges are experienced Starfleet officers returning to the Academy for more intensive study in their chosen fields. In some special cases, the graduate will be offered the opportunity to continue as a student in one of the Advanced Colleges.

Additionally, Starfleet's Direct Procurement Program, Commanding Officer's Training, Department Head School, and other specialized training opportunities for Fleet personnel are included within the framework of the College of Fleet Operations.

More detailed information on Basic Training and the Advanced Colleges may be found under the appropriate headings in this Handbook.

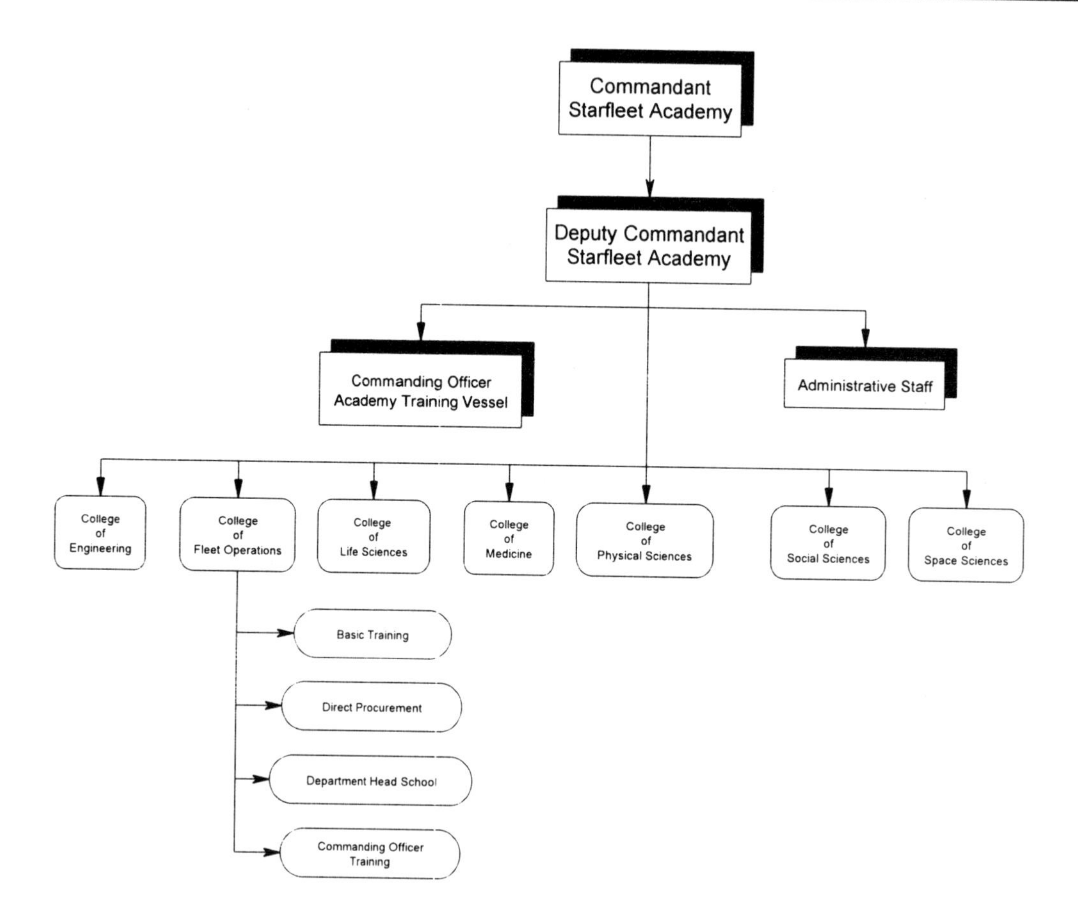


Starfleet Academy Organization Chart

# PHYSICAL LAYOUT

## Design Considerations

Early on in the campus design process, planners recognized the effects of a high–stress curriculum on the students attending Starfleet Academy. There would be constant pressure to assimilate a large amount of knowledge, a concomitant requirement to meet stringent deadlines and perform on tests while, at the same time, adapt to the unique rules and regulations of Starfleet.

Environmental design specialists were included in each architectural team and directed to make stress reduction an integral part of campus plans. A number of proposals were considered; most were discarded as unsuitable or cost prohibitive.

The most effective solution to this problem for both humanoids and non–humanoids was to ensure that the layout of each campus included a careful combination of aesthetic design and foliage to approximate a natural environment. The visual effect of large numbers of native plants and the increased levels of oxygen resulting from the photosynthesis process would produce an atmosphere with positive effects. This concept was included in the design of each campus.

## Starfleet Academy (Home Fleet)

Starfleet Academy (Home Fleet) is located on Treasure Island in San Francisco Bay. Laid out in the shape of a circle, the Main Administration Building (MAB) is in the center. Residence Hulls are on the circumference of the grounds at 90 degree points. Walkways extend from the MAB to each Hull. Paired Learning Centers face each other on either side of each walkway.

Kentucky Bluegrass is used as a ground cover on all open areas of the campus. Numerous beds of plants such as Bear's Breeches, Eryngo, Canna Lily, and Trumpet Honeysuckle provide a colorful landscape throughout the year.

Stands of Paper and European White Birch dot the campus. Several different types of trees, including Catalpa, Russian Olive, and Oak create a canopy over each walkway.

## Starfleet Academy (First Fleet)

On LoriLynn, Starfleet Academy (First Fleet) takes the shape of a square. Residence hulls are at each corner. From the Main Administration Building walkways extend out to bisect each side of the square and to connect with the Residence Hulls. Each Learning Center has a breezeway through which the walkway passes.

Bilbo's Bane, a green and white variegated ground cover native to the planet, is used instead of grass on the campus. This plant attains a height of approximately 15 centimeters and is highly resistant to traffic. Numerous beds filled with plants such as Blyewaithe, Crimson Crynkyl, and Menolly soften the sharp angles of the buildings and grounds.

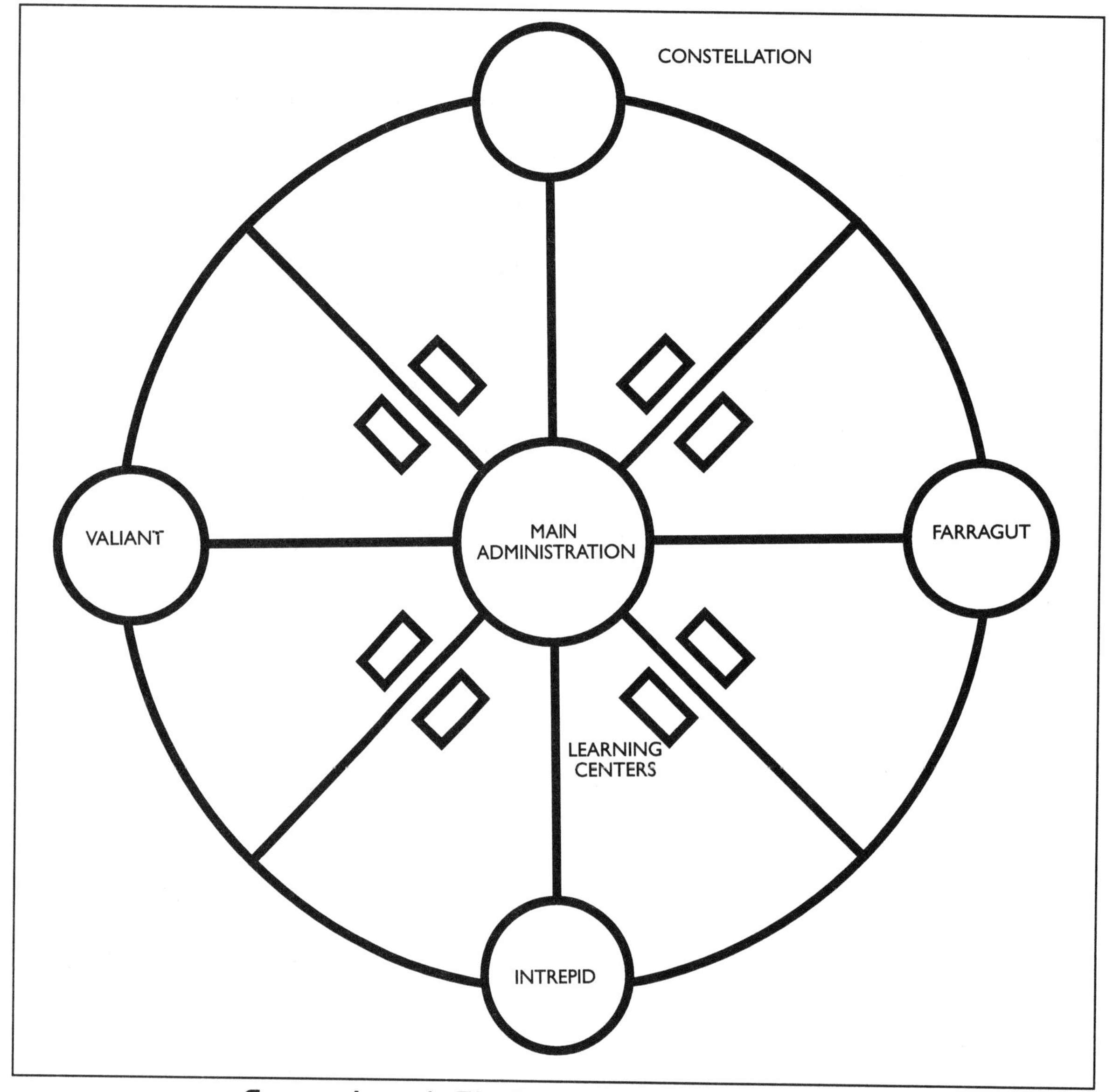


Campus Layout, Starfleet Academy (Home Fleet)

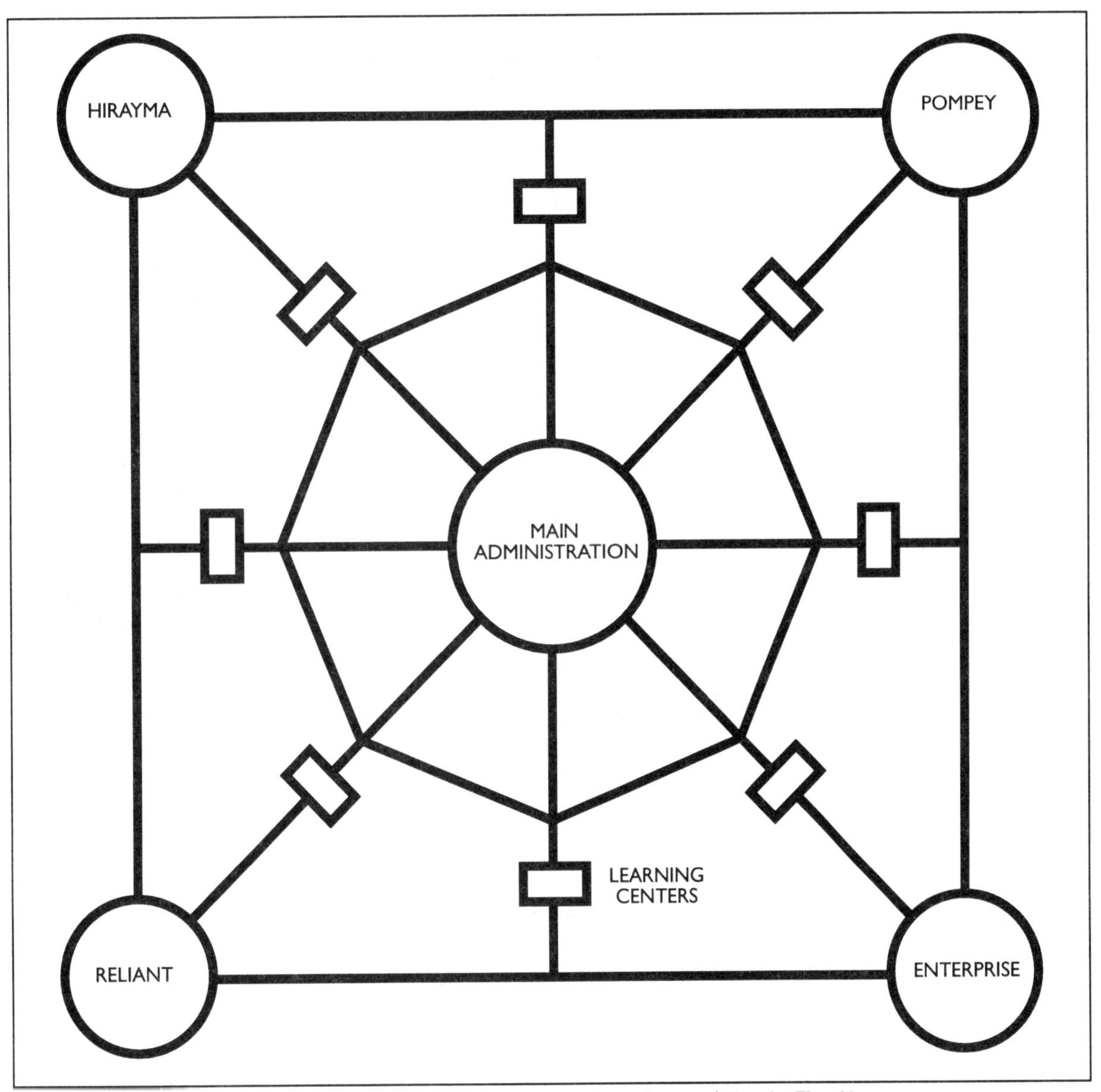


Campus Layout, Starfleet Academy (First Fleet)

## Starfleet Academy (Second Fleet)

Starfleet Academy (Second Fleet) on New Britain is laid out as a four–pointed star. A Residence Hall is located at each point. Walkways originate at the MAB and extend in a straight line to each Residence Hull. Two Learning Centers are located on opposite sides of each walkway.

In contrast to the usual clean lines at other academies, the walls of Learning Centers at Second Fleet Academy are covered by Calliope. The vibrant green leaves of this native ivy are shaped like a four–pointed star. After more than 100 years of growth, some stems have a diameter exceeding 30 centimeters.

Giant redwoods (*Sequoiadendron giganteum*) were transplanted from Earth during construction. These huge trees have adapted well to their new location and, along with several varieties of Earth oak and native Pillars of Hercules, make this campus the most arboreal of all the academies

## Starfleet Academy (Third Fleet)

A pentagon was used for the campus of Starfleet Academy (Third Fleet) on Enya. Three Resident Hulls are placed on the top three points, while the fourth bisects the base.

Learning Centers, unlike the other four campuses, are place asymmetrically around the MAB. Two are located above the MAB while the remaining six are below, at 45 degree angles, which are grouped into a complex of threes. Two Learning Centers are one either side of the walkway, while the third Learning Center contains a breezeway through which the walkway passes.

Third Fleet Academy takes advantage of its tropical location on a cliff overlooking the Oroco Flow, Enya's largest ocean. The campus has many palm–like trees, groups of gigantic ferns, and numerous lakes and reflecting pools. Many of the tree trunks are covered by Gandalf's Robes, a native climbing vine with large flowers resembling Earth's Bird of Paradise.

The campus is bounded on three sides by an almost impregnable forest of Mirkwood. These ancient trees reach a height of 150 meters or more.

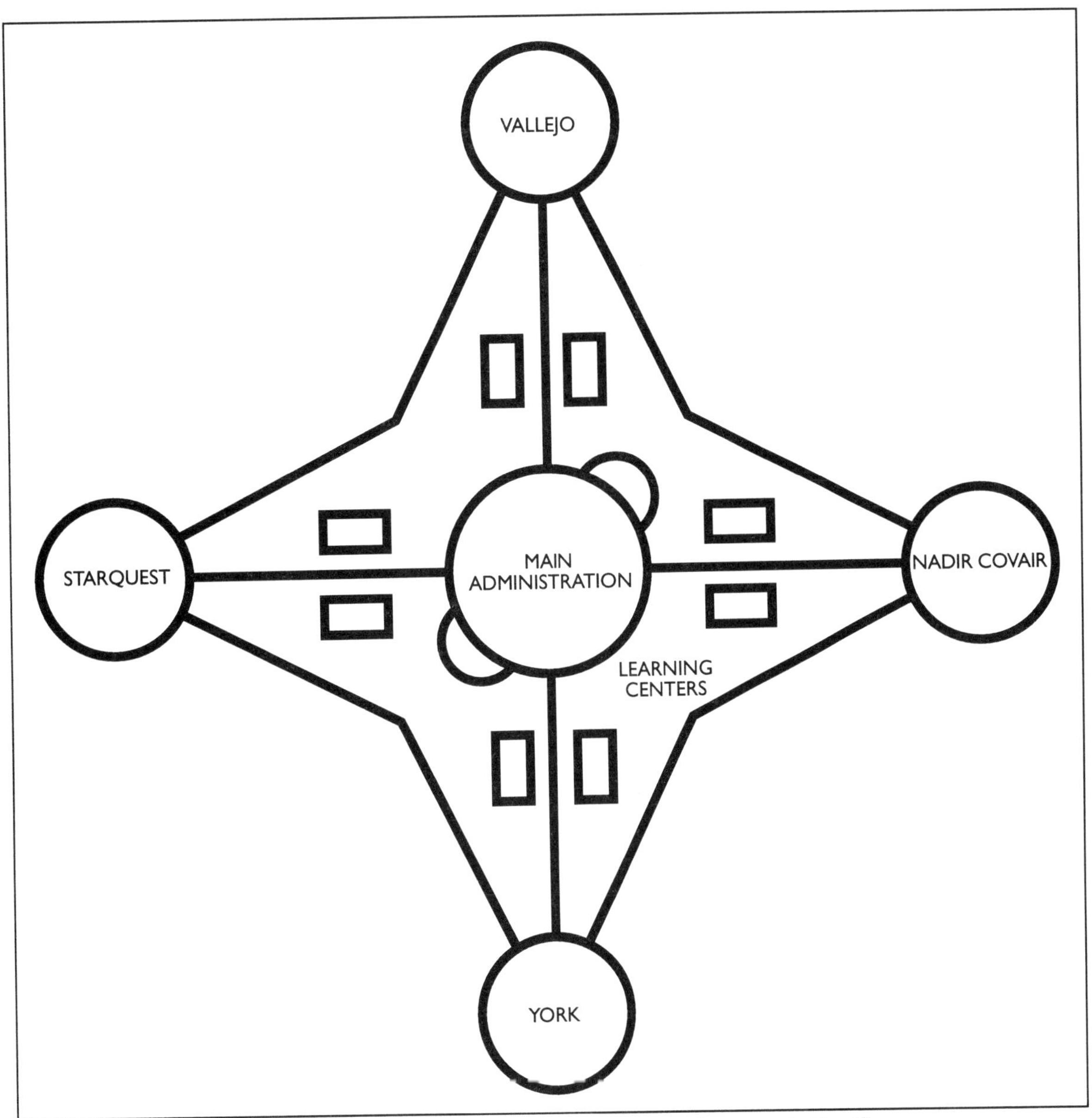


Campus Layout, Starfleet Academy (Second Fleet)

## Starfleet Academy (Fourth Fleet)

The octagon was used for the layout of Starfleet Academy (Fourth Fleet) on Avatar. Residence Hulls joined by walkways form an "X" shape at the top and bottom points. Walkways radiate from the MAB to each side's intersection. Two Learning Centers face each other across from the walkways.

Beginning with the section between the walkways between the Residence Hulls, alternate sections of the campus are constructed lakes. Each contains numerous species of fish, both native and imported. Various types of aquatic vegetation, such as King's Crowns and Beggar's Lilies, provide color year around.

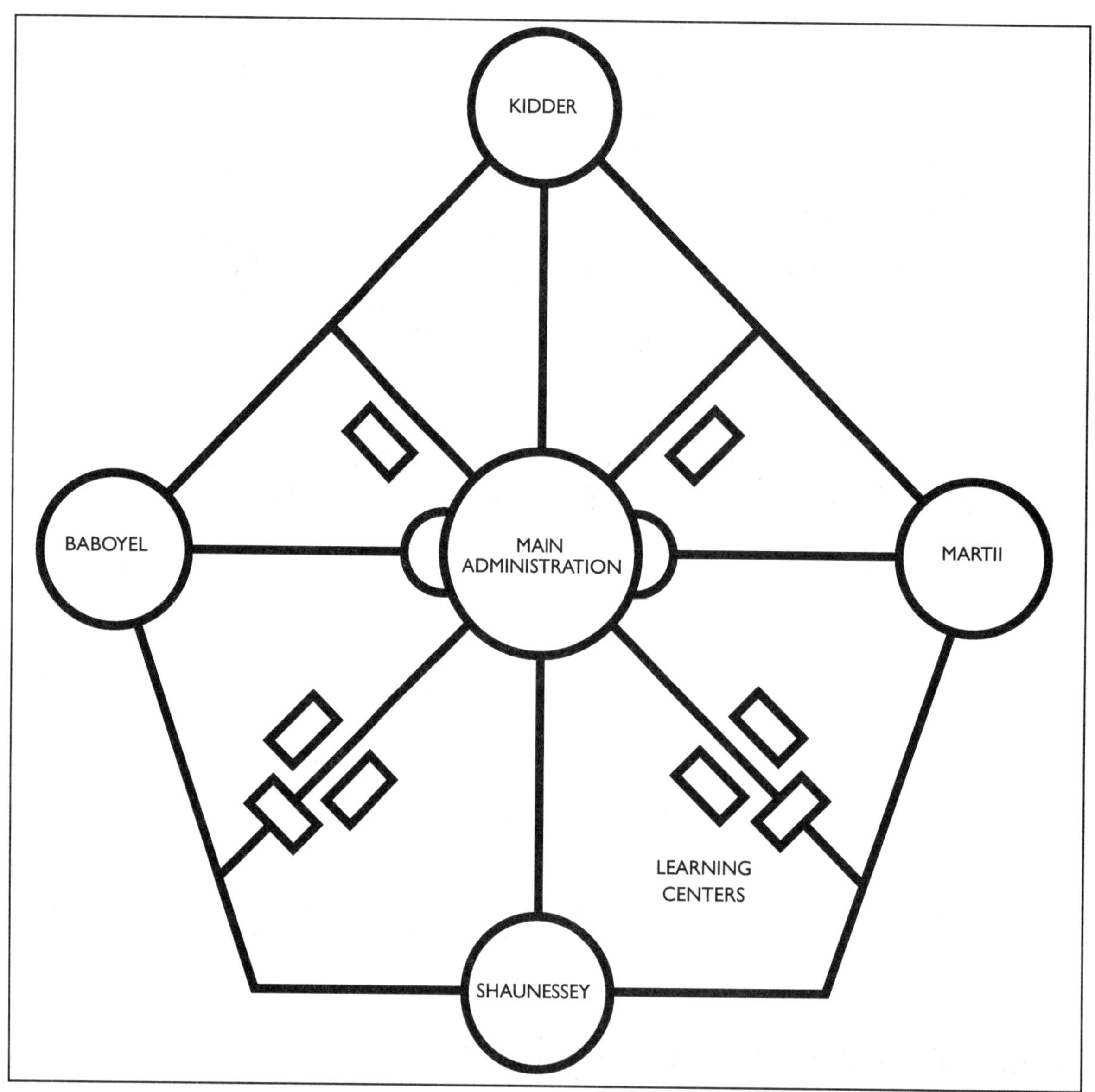


Campus Layout, Starfleet Academy (Third Fleet)

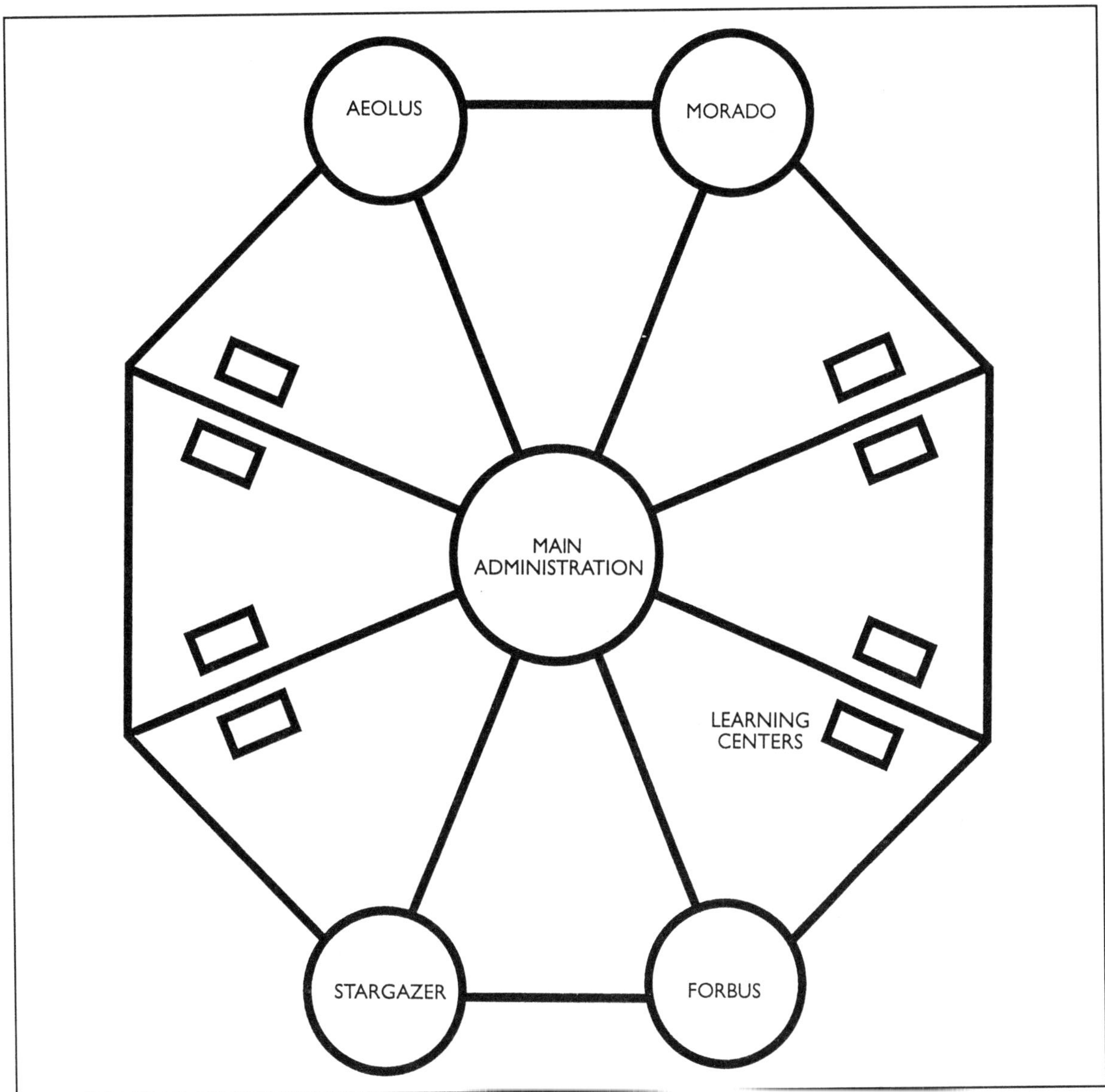


Campus Layout, Starfleet Academy (Fourth Fleet)

## Main Administration Building

The Main Administration Building (MAB), located in the center of each campus, contains all administrative offices for the Academy, including the Commandant's Office, Personnel, Career Counseling, the Main Library Computer, and medical facilities. Also included in the MAB is an auditorium for large gathering and commencement exercises.

The top floor (or deck) of each MAB is a rotating restaurant which serves as the main eating facility for faculty and staff.

Each MAB is a scaled–down replica of one of the types of starbases used by Starfleet. A Type–79 Starbase is used at Starfleet Academy (Home Fleet) and Starfleet Academy (Fourth Fleet). The REGULA–1 Starbase (Administrative type) is used at Starfleet Academy (Second Fleet and Third Fleet), while Starfleet Academy (First Fleet) is patterned after the K–7 starbase.

Surrounding the base of each MAB is a three–meter high, one–meter thick white marble wall. Plaques, engraved with the name, hull number, type, and date of commissioning for every ship in Starfleet's history, are embedded in this Wall of Honor in commissioning date order. Several openings in the Wall of Honor allow passage into the inner area.

**USS CONCORD**
**NCC 2605**
Commissioned: 7732.53
Built: Cameron Naval Facility, Deneb V

**Wall of Honor Plaque**

Within the inner area, oriented toward the main entrance to the MAB, is a smaller wall of polished Black Ironwood from the forests of Tantinum. The Wall partially encircles a reflective pool and fountain. Several benches for meditation are provided. The Wall of Memories lists every Starfleet vessel lost in the line of duty. Each plaque contains the ship's name and hull number, and the location and year of the ship's loss.

**USS STARGAZER**
**NCC 2893**
Delta Triangle
2307

**Wall of Memories Plaque**

MAB, Starfleet Academy (Second Fleet)

Entrance into the MAB is through large, transparent aluminum doors. The circular lobby has numerous sofas, chairs, and tables for the convenience of visitors waiting for escorts to their destinations. The walls (or bulkheads as they are traditionally called) are decorated with holographs of the different types of vessels in Starfleet such as Dreadnoughts, Destroyers, Heavy Cruisers, Star Cruisers, Tugs, Heavy Frigates, etc. Interspersed among these are other holographs depicting various planets in the United Federation of Planets as viewed from space. The decor contributes to the scholarly and reflective air commensurate with the role of Starfleet Academy.

A reception desk in the center of the lobby is staffed around the clock. From this station any staff member, faculty member, or student can be located within seconds. It also serves as the primary scheduling point for all activities in the Academy and provides staff, faculty, student, and visitor alike with general information about the Academy and its events.

Access to the MAB lobby is unrestricted; however, access to other areas requires an escort and a visitor's badge, which are available at the reception desk.

## Learning Centers

Each College in the Academy has a building dedicated to its classrooms and associated educational facilities. These buildings, called Learning Centers, are externally identical on each campus; however, their internal arrangement and layout reflect the requirements of specific degree programs.

Offices for the Dean of the College and the administrative staff are located on the top floor of each Learning Center. Every faculty member of the college has an office for student consultations, course development, research, and other activities.

In addition to classrooms, each Learning Center contains several holodecks. They are programmed to display significant historic events and replicate laboratory conditions for student use. Holodecks are a valuable adjunct to learning and are used extensively throughout a student's educational experience at the Academy.

In addition to classrooms and holodecks, each Learning Center has a museum room where artifacts important to the area covered by the College are displayed. The contents of these museum rooms are rotated among the five academies on a regular basis.

Learning Centers are open to students at any time for group study sessions, individual work, or extra classroom time scheduled by a faculty member. Use of the holodecks after normal class hours must be approved and scheduled in advance by a faculty member.

Typical Learning Center

## Residence Hulls

There are four separate accommodations for students attending the Academy. Each is an exact replica of the primary saucer used by most Starfleet vessels. The design of these facilities is not only aesthetic, but also acquaints Midshipmen with Starfleet living and provides a sense of identification for those students attending one of the Advanced Colleges.

Since the purpose of the Residence Hull is to provide living quarters for students, spaces occupied by engineering, science, medical, and other operational areas in an actual primary hull have been replaced by additional staterooms. The lounges, meal areas, and recreational facilities have been retained.

Each berthing facility, called a "Hull," is named for a Starfleet vessel lost in the line of duty. Each Hull, and the vessel for which it was named, are as follows:

Starfleet Academy (Home Fleet)

- Hull CONSTELLATION (NCC–1017, Heavy Cruiser)
- Hull FARRAGUT (NCC–1702, Heavy Cruiser)
- Hull INTREPID (NCC–1708, Heavy Cruiser)
- Hull VALIANT (NCC–1704, Heavy Cruiser)

Starfleet Academy (First Fleet)

- Hull ENTERPRISE (NCC–1701–Heavy Cruiser)
- Hull POMPEY (NCC–506, Destroyer)
- Hull RELIANT (NCC–1864, Heavy Frigate)
- Hull HIRAYMA (NCC–3874, Tug)

Starfleet Academy (Second Fleet)

- Hull NADIR COVAIR (NCC–275, Light Corvette
- Hull VALLEJO (NCC–174, Gunboat)
- Hull YORK (NCC–268, Light Corvette)
- Hull STARQUEST (NCC–2894, Star Cruiser)

Starfleet Academy (Third Fleet)

- Hull SHAUNESSEY (NCC–985, Light Transport/Tug)
- Hull KIDDER (NCC–683, Hospital Ship)
- Hull MARTII (NCC–4907, Heavy Destroyer)
- Hull BABOYEL (NCC–5111, Heavy Shuttle Carrier)

Starfleet Academy (Fourth Fleet)

- Hull STARGAZER (NCC–2893), Star Cruiser)
- Hull FORBUS (NCC–1962, Through–deck Cruiser)
- Hull MORADO (NCC–255, Light Corvette)
- Hull AEOLUS (NCC–5002, Scout)

Midshipman staterooms are composed of three basic units: two mirror–image sleeping quarters and a common area containing a great room and sanitary facilities. The total area of these quarters is approximately 187 square meters. Individual environmental controls allow for simulation of home world humidity, temperature, and light spectrum in the living spaces.

Entrance from the corridor is through a voice–activated or proximity–triggered door into the shared great room. Standard furniture in the great room includes two chairs, a sofa, two end tables, a coffee table and a holoscreen. Some latitude is permitted in furnishing the great room with personal items. Other furniture is available from the Academy's Quartermaster to expand the decor to coincide with individual tastes.

Sanitary facilities (commonly referred to as a "head") are reached through a door set in the bulkhead opposite the main entrance. A sonic shower is located in the center of the outer hull bulkhead. On either side of the shower are private toilet areas. Storage cabinets are located on all unused bulkheads. At each end of the head is a door which leads into one of the sleeping areas.

A walk–in closet occupies one full end of the sleeping quarters; a large bed is located at the opposite end. Clothing and personal articles can be stored under night stands on either side of the bed or in a compartment located above the mirrored headboard. A computer terminal and desk are situated on the side of the sleeping compartment opposite the head entrance.

Every computer terminal can access the Main Library Computer located in the MAB, as well as any other computer terminal on campus (with the exception of certain restricted–access stations).

At each turbolift entrance to a Hull is a plaque which commemorates the ship after which it was named.

In Honor Of
**USS MARTII**
**NCC 4907**
Heavy Destroyer

**Residence Hull Plaque**

# Berthing Assignments

Berthing assignments for Midshipmen at Starfleet Academy are multi–occupant; that is, each stateroom in a Residence Hull is shared by two students. There are three main criteria by which assignments are made:

- Cultural and social norms
- Species–specific environmental demands
- Individual personality traits

One of the basic tenets of the United Federation of Planets is the right of all sentient beings to equal treatment. By extrapolation, this concept is embodied in Starfleet by General Order #1, and is a mainstay of Starfleet Academy and is taken into consideration when berthing assignments are made.

As an example, assignments are normally non–gender specific—the student's gender is not a determining factor. However, should an individual's cultural and social norms prohibit sharing living facilities with a member of the opposite sex, such an assignment would not be made.

Every stateroom has environmental controls which reproduce almost any combination of gravity, humidity, temperature, and light spectrum found in the United Federation of Planets. This enables individuals to replicate their home world conditions, since many species have not evolved under Earth–standard conditions. To prevent the negative impact of contrasting environmental conditions which may arise due to these differences, student from non–compatible home worlds are not assigned to the same multi–occupant stateroom.

For instance, a student from a low–gravity, low–humidity home world would not be assigned quarters with a student from a high–gravity, high–humidity tropical home world. This policy ensures that the student can maintain a suitable comfort level in the privacy of their own quarters.

The last criteria for berthing assignments recognizes that individual personality traits may be incompatible. Should a student discover that the assigned co–occupant is so dissimilar in personalities that sharing living quarters will impact upon either's performance at Starfleet Academy, the Academy's Administrative Officer will investigate alternate berthing arrangements.

# TRANSPORTATION FACILITIES

Travel to and from Starfleet Academy by visitors, and faculty and staff living off campus, is accomplished by either transporter or shuttlecraft. Transporter facilities are located only in the Main Administrative Building and consist of three 23–person, standard transporter complexes.

Transporter stations are manned at all times by a console operator and a security guard. Starfleet Academy is essentially a closed campus. Other than faculty and staff movements, which are unrestricted, any use of the transporters requires special clearance and advance notification. Arrangements for special transporter use are made with the Chief Security Officer.

There are two shuttlecraft facilities at the Academy—one for student training and the other for visitors, faculty, and staff. Each Academy has 12 standard, warp–capable shuttles for its own use and 50 standard, warp–capable shuttles for student flight training.

The shuttles used for student training are named after Starfleet personnel killed or lost in the line of duty. Shuttles for faculty, staff, and visitor use are named after past Commandants of the particular Academy.

Flights to and from the Academy for visitors, faculty, and staff originate and terminate only on the Shuttle Operations Center deck of the Main Administration Building. This Center contains maintenance facilities for the Academy's shuttles and has the capability to land or launch up to five shuttlecraft simultaneously. (Shuttle flights to transport faculty and staff to and from residential areas are scheduled on a routine basis.) Clearance from the Chief Security Officer and the Flight Deck Control Officer must be obtained prior to any non–scheduled flight.

Shuttlecraft operations and maintenance facilities for students are located at the Shuttle Operations Complex located outside each campus for safety and control. These facilities are built underground so as not to impact on the planet's environment. The only visible evidence of their presence is a six–craft landing pad.

Training flights are conducted in restricted air space areas away from inhabited areas. Search–and–rescue (SAR) crews are on standby during all student training flights in case of an emergency. Student pilots must adhere to strict flight rules and remain in designated training corridors at all times. Violation of the strict flight rules under which shuttle training is conducted can result in serious repercussions.

# VISITOR POLICY

The Director of Education, Starfleet Command, has designated Starfleet Academy a closed campus, which means that the Academy is not open to visitors on a daily basis. This policy is intended to reduce student, faculty, and staff distractions. Provisions have been made, however, to allow relatives of students, high–ranking Federation officials, and Starfleet officers to visit the Academy under specific conditions. Guidelines for each category follow.

## Students

Cadets attending the Basic Program are allowed to entertain visitors during the 10–day period between each semester. Application for visitor passes and lodging accommodations are arranged through the Academy's Chief Security Officer. Except for unusual circumstances, at least 10 days advance notification is required.

Students attending one of the Advanced Colleges may receive visitors at any time during the semester. Visitor passes and lodging accommodations are arranged through the Academy's Chief Security Officer. Except for unusual circumstances, at least 10 days advance notification is required.

## Federation Officials

As a high–visibility component of Starfleet Command, Starfleet Academy often receives requests for tours of the campus from Federation member governments. Applications are made directly to the Commandant of the specific Academy. The Chief Security Officer will arrange for accommodations in one of the VIP suites in the MAB, visitor passes, and appropriate security escorts. Guided tours are scheduled by the Chief Administrative Officer. Except for unusual circumstances at least five days advanced notification is required.

## Starfleet Officers

Unofficial visits to Starfleet Academy by Starfleet officers are discouraged. However, requests with sufficient justification may be approved by the Academy's Chief Security Officer. Official visits can be accommodated with as little as one day's notice. With the exception of Flag Officers (Rear Admiral and above) who are assigned quarters in the MAB, accommodations will be provided in one of the Residence Hulls.

# PROTOCOL

A Midshipman in Starfleet Academy is in constant training to become a competent Starfleet officer. Protocol is, therefore, emphasized in every aspect of Academy life. The faculty and staff of Starfleet Academy are composed of Starfleet officers, Starfleet enlisted personnel, and civilians. Each must be treated with the respect commensurate with their positions.

An officer in Starfleet serves among other officers and over enlisted personnel. Some officers are superiors, some are equals, some subordinates. All enlisted personnel are subordinates. There are different forms and ways of interacting with each, depending upon relative status. However, the common factor is courtesy. Treating fellow personnel with proper respect is an essential part of being an officer.

An officer is a peer among other officers; however, some formalities do pertain. When addressing or greeting a superior officer, he or she is addressed by rank and last name, or simply by rank ("Captain Clayton" or "Captain"). An officer of equal rank is addressed by rank, rank and last name, or, if the individual has given permission, by first name ("Lieutenant," "Lieutenant Kylye," or "Jon").

A subordinate officer is addressed by rank, rank and last name, the title "Mister," the title Mister and last name, or, if permission has been given, by first name ("Ensign," "Ensign Peters," "Mister Peters," or "Kevin").

A Petty Officer is addressed by the rating, or rating and last name ("Petty Officer," or "Petty Officer Williams"). Chief Petty Officers are referred to by the title "Chief," or Chief and last name ("Chief" or "Chief Brown"). A Senior Chief Petty Officer is referred to by the title "Senior Chief," or Senior Chief and name ("Senior Chief" or "Senior Chief Brown"). A Master Chief Petty Officer is referred to by the title "Master Chief," or Master Chief and last name ("Master Chief" or "Master Chief Burke").

When a superior gives an order, the correct response by the subordinate is "Aye, aye, sir." The superior may respond "Very well," or "Very good," but not the subordinate. "Aye, aye, sir" means three things:

- I heard the order
- I understand the order
- I will carry it out to the best of my ability

Civilian instructors at Starfleet Academy may be addressed by title ("Doctor Bock" or "Professor Bock"), or as "Mister" (the honorific "Mister" is not considered to be gender specific). In more informal situations, the individual may be addressed by first name or nickname, so long as specific permission has been given.

# UNIFORMS

During normal class hours, male midshipmen at Starfleet Academy wear the Standard Duty Uniform Option 1 or, standard Duty Uniform Option 2 for females. Graduation ceremonies and other special circumstances require the use of Ceremonial Dress uniforms. Civilian clothes may be worn during authorized periods as specified by the Commandant.

Rank insignia for midshipmen shall be worn in the same manner as commissioned Starfleet officers, on the right side of the uniform collar. Composed of one, two, three, or four black "pips," the individual's relative status is readily apparent. The higher the number of "pips," the higher the seniority.

# LEAVE AND LIBERTY

The unique nature of attendance at Starfleet Academy requires a modification to the normal leave and liberty regulations of Starfleet which are explained in the Starfleet Personnel Manual.

There are two classes of leave: regular and emergency. Regular leave is a period of time away from Starfleet Academy with no obligation to attend classes or other Academy functions. Emergency leave is available to individuals for specific circumstances detailed in Starfleet Personnel Manual. Leave is earned at a rate of 192 hours per semester. A 10–day period between semesters is available for students to avail themselves of accumulated leave.

Liberty is defined as time away from Starfleet Academy studies; that is, time when the student is not required to attend classes or other specified academic functions. There are no travel restrictions placed on liberty, so long as the individual is able to attend classes on time, or respond as necessary to the requirements of faculty or staff. An individual is considered to be on liberty anytime he or she is not obligated to attend classes or appear as directed by faculty or staff.

# PROMOTIONS

A beginning Midshipman is classified as a Midshipman Fourth Class. Upon successful completion of the first year of studies, the individual is automatically promoted to Midshipman Third Class. Similarly, a student in the third year of studies is a Midshipman Second Class; and a student in the final year of studies is a Midshipman First Class. These promotions are automatic in nature, so long as all classes are successfully completed. For rank insignia for each Class, see the section on Uniforms.

Upon graduation, a student is promoted to the brevet rank of Ensign.

# GRADUATION

Commencement ceremonies are held each year at the end of the fourth semester. As one would expect, it is an occasion filled with both joy and trepidation. For it is at graduation that a student will agree to uphold the traditions and laws of Starfleet and the United Federation of Planets, be promoted to the brevet rank of Ensign, and begin a career in Starfleet. Duty orders are put into effect and the student will be able to take any accumulated leave en route to the specified duty station.

# DUTY ASSIGNMENTS

Students complete a Duty Preference form during the first semester of their fourth year at the Academy. This form allows the individual to express a preference for their first duty station or indicate the general area in which they would like to be stationed. However, the needs of Starfleet are of paramount importance and supersede personal preferences. Duty orders are posted 40 days prior to graduation. There are four categories of duty assignments: starship, Starbase, planetary, and special.

Starship duty can be aboard one of two types of ships: mobile and deployed. Mobile ships include vessels which are not ordinarily absent from a homeport for extended periods of time. Deployed ships may be sent on missions of up to five years. Examples of mobile units are Tugs, Transports, Hospital Ships and defense Fighter units. Ships classified as deployed units include Star Cruisers, Heavy Cruisers, Penetration Cruisers, and Strike Cruisers.

Orders to a Starbase are the second category of duty. The assignment may be to a Starbase in orbit around a planet or to one positioned at a strategic location in space, or on the surface of a planet. This category is further divided into staff personnel and base personnel. Staff personnel are individuals who provide administrative and operational support to Fleet headquarters and higher–echelon commands, while base personnel are involved in the day–to–day operations of the Starbase itself.

Selection for advanced training at Starfleet Academy, assignment to Research and Development facilities, and to Starfleet shipyards are examples of the third category of duty orders: Planetary duty. Also in this category is assignment to Starfleet Command.

The last category of duty orders is called Special Duty. Orders to Starfleet Intelligence, the Inspector General's office, or Test and Evaluation units (for example, Cathedral Unit) all fall into this classification. Individuals may also be ordered to Honor Guard or Special Security Forces.

For a more detailed explanation of each assignment category, refer to the Starfleet Personnel Manual.

The orders will include the name of the station, the type of duty (starship, Starbase, planetary, or special), the commanding officer's name, and the location of the duty station. Each set of orders includes time for the individual to take accumulated leave en route; however, should the individual desire to take a lesser amount of leave than authorized in the orders, arrangements can be made to modify the reporting time through the Personnel Office. Extensions of the reporting time can be effected only through the use of Emergency Leave, a category of leave reserved for family emergencies.

# TIMEKEEPING

The natural habitat of a starship is deep space where there is no planetary rotation to provide a convenient method of measuring the passage of time. The Academy is designed to prepare officers for starship duty and, therefore, utilizes the 24–hour clock to mark the passage of time. This 24–hour clock is tied to Universal Standard Time, maintained at the London Observatory, London, (Earth).

The 24–hour clock is also used to eliminate any possible confusion in establishing the time of an occurrence, whether it be current or scheduled. The hours begin at 0030 (12:30 AM) and count up through 2400 (midnight). This cycle is repeated continuously.

Many ships in Starfleet also use the system of "bells," first established on 18th Century Earth sailing ships, to mark the passage of time. Beginning at 0030 with one tone (which sounds similar to the ring of a bell), each half hour of the day and night is marked by an increasing number of tones. The number of "bells" sounded after eight, begin again at one. Therefore, each half hour is indicated by an odd number of bells, and each hour is marked by an even number of bells. A convenient chart to clarify the number of bells and their equivalent times on both the 24–hour clock and 12–hour clock is provided.

# CLASS SCHEDULE

The academic year is 400 days in length. It is divided into four semesters of 100 days each. Students will attend classes from 0700 to 1650 each day for eight days. Following the last class on the eighth day, students will have two days off for rest and relaxation or study.

The final 10–day period of a semester is available for students to take accumulated leave or receive visitors.

During class days, a two–hour period is provided for the mid–day meal, from 1100 to 1300. The following is the class schedule:

| | |
|---|---|
| 0700–0750 | Class |
| 0800–0850 | Class |
| 0900–0950 | Class |
| 1000–1050 | Class |
| 1100–1300 | Lunch |
| 1300–1350 | Class |
| 1400–1450 | Class |
| 1500–1550 | Class |
| 1600–1650 | Class |

| 24–hr Clock | Equivalent | Bells | 24–hr Clock | Equivalent | Bells |
|---|---|---|---|---|---|
| 0030 | :30 AM | 1 | 1230 | 12:30 PM | 1 |
| 0100 | 1:00 AM | 2 | 1300 | 1:00 PM | 2 |
| 0130 | 1:30 AM | 3 | 1330 | 1:30 PM | 3 |
| 0200 | 2:00 AM | 4 | 1400 | 2:00 PM | 4 |
| 0230 | 2:30 AM | 5 | 1430 | 2:30 PM | 5 |
| 0300 | 3:00 AM | 6 | 1500 | 3:00 PM | 6 |
| 0330 | 3:30 AM | 7 | 1530 | 3:30 PM | 7 |
| 0400 | 4:00 AM | 8 | 1600 | 4:00 PM | 8 |
| 0430 | 4:30 AM | 1 | 1630 | 4:30 PM | 1 |
| 0500 | 5:00 AM | 2 | 1700 | 5:00 PM | 2 |
| 0530 | 5:30 AM | 3 | 1730 | 5:30 PM | 3 |
| 0600 | 6:00 AM | 4 | 1800 | 6:00 PM | 4 |
| 0630 | 6:30 AM | 5 | 1830 | 6:30 PM | 5 |
| 0700 | 7:00 AM | 6 | 1900 | 7:00 PM | 6 |
| 0730 | 7:30 AM | 7 | 1930 | 7:30 PM | 7 |
| 0800 | 8:00 AM | 8 | 2000 | 8:00 PM | 8 |
| 0830 | 8:30 AM | 1 | 2030 | 8:30 PM | 1 |
| 0900 | 9:00 AM | 2 | 2100 | 9:00 PM | 2 |
| 0930 | 9:30 AM | 3 | 2130 | 9:30 PM | 3 |
| 1000 | 10:00 AM | 4 | 2200 | 10:00 PM | 4 |
| 1030 | 10:30 AM | 5 | 2230 | 10:30 PM | 5 |
| 1100 | 11:00 AM | 6 | 2300 | 11:00 PM | 6 |
| 1130 | 11:30 AM | 7 | 2330 | 11:30 PM | 7 |
| 1200 | NOON | 8 | 0000 | MIDNIGHT | 8 |

# BASIC PROGRAM

Starfleet Academy's Basic Program is designed to provide prospective Starfleet officers with a basic understanding of the organization, its members, its rules and regulations, and provide a base for the development of the camaraderie so essential to a successful career in Starfleet. The graduate will be a Starfleet officer who possesses the appropriate skills to:

- operate successfully within the paradigm of a military career
- interact with other sentient beings in a manner commensurate with the concepts of the Articles of Federation as well as the regulations of Starfleet
- conduct themselves in a manner which will uphold the long and proud history of Starfleet and the United Federation of Planets
- and retain a basic individuality reflecting the culture and background which accompanied the individual to Starfleet Academy

## GENERAL INFORMATION

The Bachelor of Science program at Starfleet Academy offers a degree in one of the following majors:

- Engineering
- Life Sciences
- Medicine
- Physical Sciences
- Social Sciences
- Space Sciences

## ELIGIBILITY

Starfleet is in constant need of new personnel. Retirements, releases from duty, and other considerations continuously impact on the manning requirements for the starbases and starships of Starfleet. Although the requirements vary as the political and military situation in the United Federation of Planets fluctuates, approximately six percent of Starfleet personnel leave the service each Earth Calendar Year. Any citizen of the United Federation of Planets, regardless of race, creed, nationality, or parent–world affiliation, may apply for admission into Starfleet Academy.

# APPLICATION PROCEDURES

Applicants must complete an Application for Admission, which includes the required forms for acceptance into Starfleet, and submit it to the local UFP Liaison Office. Transcripts from all educational institutions must be included as well as four personal letters of recommendation from community or educational leaders attesting to the applicant's capabilities and past performance.

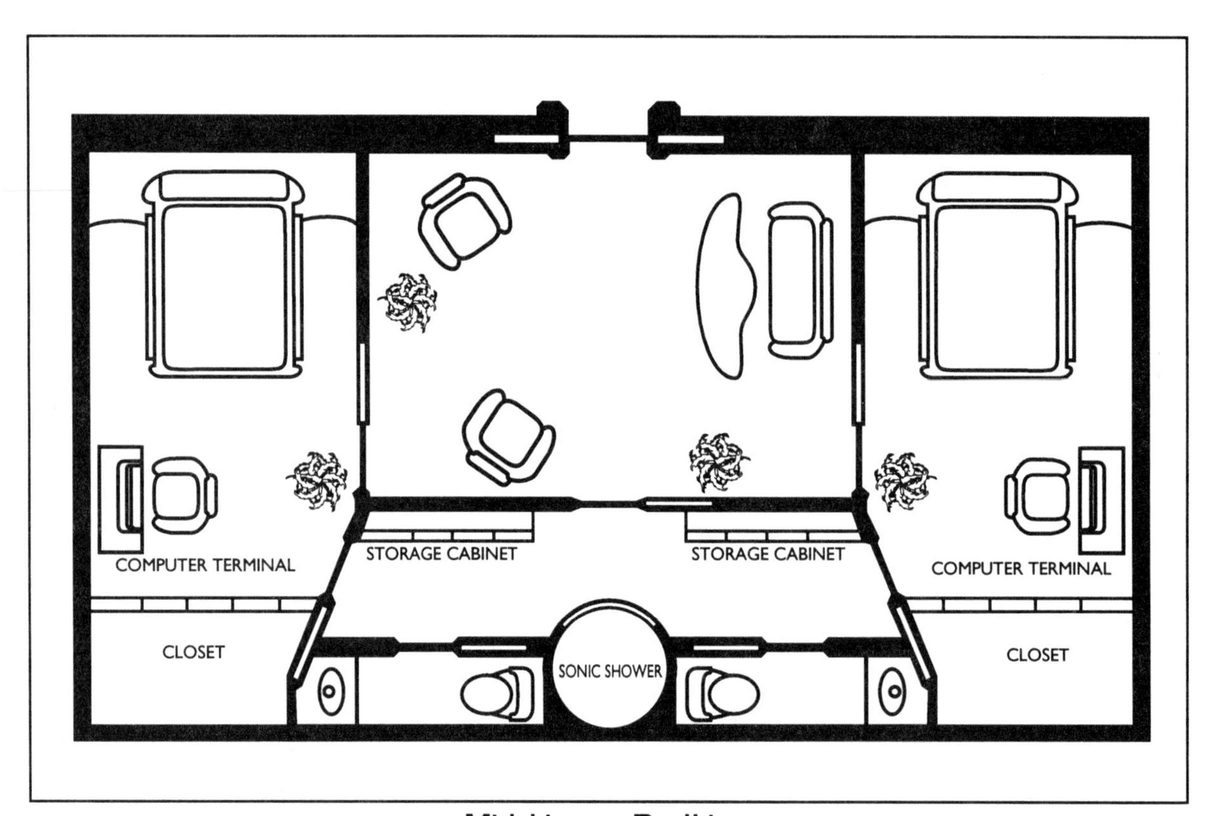


**Midshipman Berthing**

Once received by the Liaison Office and checked for completeness, all applications are forwarded to the Director of Education, Starfleet Command, where they are reviewed by a special Starfleet Personnel Acquisition Panel. Applications which are approved by this panel are then scheduled for the Starfleet Academy Entrance Examination.

These examinations are held once per Earth year at specified locations throughout the UFP. Each is composed of several sections designed to measure the applicant's past contributions as well as their ability to make future ones. Included among the topics covered in the Starfleet Academy Entrance Examination are:

- Logic
- UFP History
- Mathematics
- Literature
- Cognitive Skills
- Manual Skills
- Life Sciences
- Social Sciences
- Space Sciences
- Physical Sciences

The typical Entrance Examination requires four consecutive days to complete. The Examination is graded and a ranking of scores from all applicants taking the test is established. This ranking is consolidated with the results of the Application review and the resulting new list is used to notify candidates of their acceptance into Starfleet Academy.

An individual not selected for admission to Starfleet Academy will be notified immediately. This notification will include the reasons for non–acceptance as well as suggested actions to strengthen a future application. There is no limitation to the number of times an individual may apply for admission to Starfleet and Starfleet Academy.

Additional information on the admissions and acceptance procedures may be obtained from a local UFP Liaison Office.

# POST-ACCEPTANCE PROCEDURES

Notification of acceptance into Starfleet Academy will come through personal contact by the local Starfleet Liaison Officer. Shortly after that, the Office of Student Affairs of the Academy which the student will attend will provide additional information including transportation arrangements, the name and biography of the assigned mentor, a listing of allowed and prohibited personal items at the Academy, and other important details.

Transportation to the Academy will be accomplished by one of, or a combination of, methods: on board a Starfleet vessel which is scheduled to be in the vicinity of the students' residence planet, passage on a commercial vessel such as a freighter, or on board a passenger liner.

In any case, it is the individual's responsibility to meet all departure and connection times. Failure to meet travel arrangements is a serious situation. The traveler must contact a Starfleet Liaison Office immediately for assistance if difficulties in travel arise.

Upon arrival at the Academy, the student will undergo an indoctrination and administrative period. A number of necessary tasks will be accomplished during this time.

Berthing assignments into one of the Residence hulls will be made and time to stow personal belongings will be available. After this, uniforms will be issued and instructions as to their proper wear and maintenance will be given.

Every entrant will receive a complete medical examination. This will establish a baseline physical condition, identifying any significant characteristics or difficulties which must be addressed during the student's time at the Academy. A required immunization program will also be started.

An upper classman, either a Midshipman Second Class or Midshipman First Class, will escort a group of the entering class on a tour of the Academy's facilities. This tour will include the Residence Hulls, areas of the Main Administration Building, and the various Learning Centers. Off–campus installations, such as the Shuttle Operations Complex, will be included in this guided tour.

Each individual will meet with their assigned faculty mentor who will assist the student throughout the four years at the Academy. This initial conference provides an opportunity for the student and the mentor to become acquainted. The mentor will also discuss the student's academic plans as well as expectations and goals for a Starfleet career.

Starfleet personnel and pay records will be developed for each student. Each Midshipman will also be advised of various alternatives as far as the disposition of pay is concerned, including allotments and allowable deductions.

Briefings on the Academy's policies and procedures will be held. These briefings will explain such subjects as leave, liberty, probation, promotions, and available personal services. Attendance is mandatory.

The indoctrination period, once completed, should answer the majority of questions. The Office of Student Affairs and the Career Enhancement Office, both located in the Main Administration Building, can provide additional details if necessary.

Classes will commence on the third day following completion of the indoctrination and administrative program.

# DEGREE PROGRAMS

Prior to the beginning of the first semester of the second year at the Academy, each student must declare a major. This is an important decision which will have a major impact on the remainder of the individuals' Starfleet career.

If, before the end of the second semester, a student has not chosen a major, contact must be made with the individual's mentor, the Career Enhancement Office, or perhaps a Starfleet officer attending one of the Advanced Colleges for assistance.

Each major has 15 required courses which must be taken as electives. Available majors are: Engineering, Life Sciences, Medicine, Physical Sciences, Social Sciences, and Space Sciences.

USS UNIFICATION (NCC-2140)

The remaining six elective courses are chosen by the student from areas other than the declared major. With the exception of Medicine, at least one course from each area must be taken.

A listing of the required courses in each major is provided in the Degree Program section. Topics covered in each course are listed by course number in the section on Course Contents.

## Engineering

The field of Engineering is a dynamic environment fueled by constant innovations and new developments. This major is designed to acquaint the student with basic concepts applicable to the wide range of responsibilities inherent in a position within a starship's Engineering Department. Follow–on specialities are available in the College of Engineering for those contemplating advanced study at the MS and PhD levels. The following courses must be completed for the major in Engineering:

SFA 008 Replicator Systems
SFA 027 Transporter Systems
SFA 089 Environmental Systems
SFA 108 Deflector Shields
SFA 110 Shipboard Phasers
SFA 137 Photon Torpedoes
SFA 161 Reaction Control Systems
SFA 163 Engineering Operations and Safety
SFA 164 Remote Sensing Packages
SFA 195 Impulse Propulsion System
SFA 296 Utilities Networks
SFA 393 Warp Propulsion System I
SFA 394 Warp Propulsion System II
SFA 400 Auxiliary Systems
SFA 497 Selected Topics in Engineering

## Life Sciences

Life exists throughout the galaxy in a myriad of forms, each seemingly more complex than the one before. This major concentrates on the commonalities shared throughout a wide range of manifestations. The graduate of this program will have gained a valuable base from which to begin the study of life. Follow–on specialities are available in the College of Life Sciences for those contemplating advanced study at the MS and PhD levels. The following courses must be completed for the major in Life Sciences:

SFA 011 Principles of Systematic Biology
SFA 024 Herpetology
SFA 095 Biological Oceanography
SFA 139 Bioenergetics
SFA 155 Introduction to Botany
SFA 185 Analysis of Development
SFA 196 Ichthyology
SFA 269 Ornithology
SFA 272 Ecology
SFA 292 Mammalogy
SFA 302 Anthropology
SFA 303 Biological Chemistry
SFA 320 Selected Topics in Life Sciences
SFA 329 Biology
SFA 420 Hexapodology

USS WILDFIRE (NCC-2027)

# Medicine

Graduates of the Medicine curriculum of Starfleet Academy's Basic Program are designated a Registered Nurse. Applications to continue studies in the College of Medicine's Doctor of Medicine (MD) program will be reviewed and, if selected, the pre–med student will automatically be scheduled to attend the Advanced College. The following courses must be completed for the major in Medicine:

SFA 001 Physiological Psychology I
SFA 002 Physiological Psychology II
SFA 083 Medicolegal Investigation
SFA 105 Infectious Diseases
SFA 138 Emergency Medicine
SFA 147 Psychotherapy
SFA 186 Pharmacology
SFA 276 Clinical Laboratory Methods
SFA 285 Care Procedures
SFA 366 Anatomy I
SFA 367 Anatomy II
SFA 372 Adolescent Health Care
SFA 377 Geriatric Medicine
SFA 450 Nutrition
SFA 458 Physical Examinations

# Physical Sciences

Physical Sciences majors study the inanimate nature of planets from deep within their surface to the atmosphere. A major in this program will introduce the student to the many types of land, liquids, and gases which can be found on planets. Follow–on specialities are available in the College of Physical Sciences for those contemplating advanced study at the MS and PhD levels. The following courses must be completed for the major in Physical Sciences:

SFA 022 Introduction to Solid–State Chemistry
SFA 038 Pattern Recognition and Analysis
SFA 045 Oceanography
SFA 057 Introduction to Geology
SFA 165 Principles of Axiomatic Design
SFA 249 Topics in Nonlinear Dynamics of Dissapative Systems
SFA 260 Relativistic Quantum Field Theory

SFA 272 Fundamentals of Ecology
SFA 299 Landsurface–Atmosphere Interactions
SFA 304 Structural Mechanics
SFA 363 Selected Topics in Physical Sciences
SFA 406 Biogeography
SFA 410 Physical Methods in Inorganic Chemistry
SFA 437 Systematic Climatology
SFA 480 Defects in Crystals

## Social Sciences

An important aspect of Starfleet life is the understanding of interactions among and between sentient beings. Lifeforms express their individualities in a number of ways, creating a fertile field for the social scientist. Follow–on specialities are available in the College of Social Sciences for those contemplating advanced study at the MS and PhD levels. The following courses must be completed for the major in Social Sciences:

SFA 023 Law, Technology, and Public Policy
SFA 079 Urban Design
SFA 085 Selected Topics in Social Sciences
SFA 092 Individuals, Groups and Organizations
SFA 096 Political Development
SFA 099 Federation Political Economy
SFA 104 The Society of Mind
SFA 150 Art as Meaning and Technique
SFA 188 Modernism and Mass Culture
SFA 208 Dimensions in Space
SFA 381 Projects in Knowledge Representations
SFA 384 Introduction to Psychology
SFA 397 Interstellar Shipping
SFA 436 Comparative Value Systems
SFA 463 Economics of Uncertainty

## Space Sciences

Stars are the powerhouses of the universe. How these massive energy producers interact with each other and with stellar bodies such as planets is the realm upon which the specialist in space sciences concentrates. Follow–on specialities are available in the College of Space Sciences for those contemplating advanced study at the MS and PhD levels. The following courses must be completed for the major in Space Sciences:

| | |
|---|---|
| SFA 016 | Physics of the Galaxy |
| SFA 030 | Shipboard Sensor Systems |
| SFA 051 | Cosmology |
| SFA 070 | Stellar System Dynamics |
| SFA 102 | Selected Topics in Space Sciences |
| SFA 179 | Essentials of Planetary Science |
| SFA 187 | Chaos and Complexity |
| SFA 194 | Plasmas |
| SFA 305 | Planetary Systems |
| SFA 352 | High–Energy Astrophysics |
| SFA 370 | Stellar Structure and Evolution |
| SFA 401 | Asteroids and Small Bodies |
| SFA 451 | Particle Physics |
| SFA 474 | Continuum Mechanics |
| SFA 476 | Astrophysics |

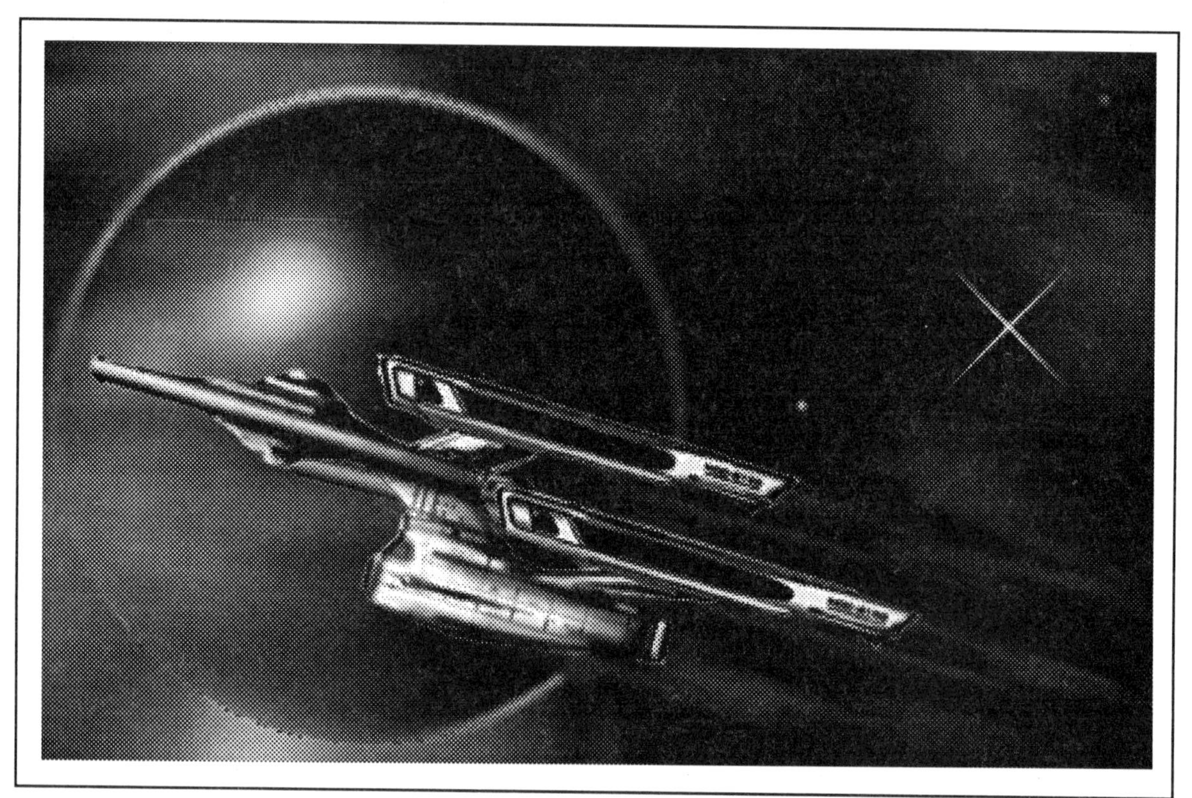

USS PROCYON (NCC-1756)

# GRADING SYSTEM

Initially, students at Starfleet Academy were not given grades; each class was either pass or fail. Within a short period of time, it became obvious that one unintended consequence of this policy was a lack of motivation on the part of Academy students. Since there was no competition for grades, students quickly reached a point where they were doing "just enough to get by."

This situation resulted in a lowering of the knowledge and abilities of graduates. It also negatively impacted the level of competitiveness of Starfleet officers—a trait always considered to be extremely valuable. Therefore, a point system was instituted to indicate a student's classroom achievements.

Each class in the curriculum is worth 1,000 points, and every student begins each class with this number of points. Based on a paradigm developed by each professor, points are deducted throughout the class. These deductions are based on the individual's performance as objectively measured on a daily basis.

Point totals are continuously updated and posted for the students' information. A semester class standing (taking into consideration all classes attended during that semester) is entered in the students' academic records. A final class standing is computed at graduation for every student.

A student must have a minimum of 750 points in a class to complete a class successfully. Those individuals with fewer than 750 points in a class must complete additional work in order to reach that level.

The chart below indicates the minimum number of points required in each year of Academy attendance.

| Year | Points |
|---|---|
| First | 24,000 |
| Second | 19,500 |
| Third | 19,500 |
| Fourth | 18,000 |
| **Total for Graduation** | 81,000 |

# ADVANCED TRAINING

A small number of students in each graduating class are presented with the opportunity to continue study in one of the Advanced Colleges. Approximately 10 percent of the Basic Programs' graduates are carefully screened for advanced training. Those who successfully pass this screening process may enroll for an MS program in one of the Advanced Colleges.

# CURRICULUM

The following pages outline, by year and semester, those courses which each student must take. Electives are indicated by italics.

Typical Learning Center

## First Year

### Semester I

SFA 111 Starfleet Orientation I
SFA 112 UFP History
SFA 113 Physical Training I
SFA 114 Language I
SFA 115 Computers I
SFA 116 Personal Combat I
SFA 117 Artistic Expression I
*Social Science Elective*

### Semester II

SFA 121 Starfleet Orientation II
SFA 122 Military Science I
SFA 123 Physical Training II
SFA 124 Language II
SFA 125 Computers II
SFA 126 Personal Combat II
SFA 127 Artistic Expression II
*Life Sciences Elective*

### Semester III

SFA 131 First Aid
SFA 132 Physical Training III
SFA 133 Nonlinear Dynamics and Chaos
SFA 134 Personal Combat III
SFA 135 Military Science II
SFA 136 Computers III
*Space Sciences Elective*
*Engineering Elective*

### Semester IV

SFA 141 Communications
SFA 142 Physical Training IV
SFA 143 Complexity Theory
SFA 144 Personal Combat IV
SFA 145 Away Team Operations
SFA 146 Computers IV
*Physical Sciences Elective*
*Free Elective*

## Second Year

### Semester I

SFA 211 Physical Training V
SFA 212 Survival Training I
SFA 213 Engineering I
SFA 214 Damage Control I
SFA 215 Remote Sensing Packages
SFA 216 Political Science I
SFA 217 Artistic Expression III
*Major Elective*

### Semester II

SFA 221 Physical Training VI
SFA 222 Survival Training II
SFA 223 Engineering II
SFA 224 Damage Control II
SFA 225 Time–Series Analysis
SFA 226 Political Science II
SFA 227 Artistic Expression IV
*Major Elective*

### Semester III

SFA 231 Physical Training VII
SFA 232 Survival Training III
SFA 233 Diophantine Geometry
SFA 234 Lie Groups
SFA 235 Starfleet Vessel Characteristics
SFA 236 Logistics in Starfleet
SFA 237 Starbase Operations
*Major Elective*

### Semester IV

SFA 241 Fast Cruise
SFA 242 Survival Experience

## Third Year

### Semester I

| | |
|---|---|
| SFA 311 | Physical Training VIII |
| SFA 312 | Commercial Vessels |
| SFA 313 | Science I |
| SFA 314 | Basic Security Operations |
| SFA 315 | Bridge Systems |
| SFA 316 | Starfleet History |
| | *Major Elective* |
| | *Major Elective* |

### Semester II

| | |
|---|---|
| SFA 321 | Physical Training IX |
| SFA 322 | Programming Models |
| SFA 323 | Science II |
| SFA 324 | Individual Ship Tactics |
| SFA 325 | Strategy and Tactics I |
| SFA 326 | Decision Analysis |
| | *Major Elective* |
| | *Major Elective* |

### Semester III

| | |
|---|---|
| SFA 331 | Physical Training X |
| SFA 332 | Strategy and Tactics II |
| SFA 333 | Tactical Weapons |
| SFA 334 | Advanced Security Operations |
| SFA 335 | Life Support Systems |
| SFA 336 | Emergency Procedures |
| | *Major Elective* |
| | *Major Elective* |

### Semester IV

| | |
|---|---|
| SFA 341 | Fast Cruise |
| SFA 342 | Current Topics |

## Fourth Year

### Semester I

| | |
|---|---|
| SFA 411 | Physical Training XI |
| SFA 412 | War and War Prevention |
| SFA 413 | Shuttlecraft Ops I |
| SFA 414 | Intercultural Relations I |
| SFA 415 | Federal Law I |
| SFA 416 | Diplomacy I |
| | *Major Elective* |
| | *Major Elective* |

### Semester II

| | |
|---|---|
| SFA 421 | Physical Training XII |
| SFA 422 | Technical Communications |
| SFA 423 | Shuttlecraft Ops II |
| SFA 424 | Intercultural Relations II |
| SFA 425 | Federal Law II |
| SFA 426 | Diplomacy II |
| | *Major Elective* |
| | *Major Elective* |

### Semester III

| | |
|---|---|
| SFA 431 | Training Cruise |

### Semester IV

| | |
|---|---|
| SFA 441 | Physical Training XIII |
| SFA 442 | Ethics |
| SFA 443 | First Contacts |
| SFA 444 | Diplomacy III |
| SFA 445 | Logic |
| SFA 446 | Command and Control |
| | *Major Elective* |
| | *Major Elective* |

# FAST CRUISES

An underground complex accessible from the Fleet Operations Learning Center holds USS NEVERSAIL (NCC–0000). It replicates major shipboard systems common to Starfleet vessels. Included in this facility are mock–ups of a Main Bridge, a Warp Engine Room, Impulse Engine Room, Science laboratories, Weapons Complex, Hydroponics Room, Sensor and Torpedo Maintenance Rooms, and other critical areas.

USS NEVERSAIL (NCC–0000) is designed to recreate shipboard situations via computer simulation. As students rotate through each station, they are familiarized with the layout, appearance, and controls of major systems. During the fast cruise, every facet of actual shipboard life is recreated. Each student is assigned to a watch section, a typical ship's schedule is followed, and the students are required to follow these simulations exactly.

In addition to normal day–to–day operations, low– to medium–level emergency situations are interjected on a random basis. Since no possibilities exist for life–threatening situations to occur, the student is able to develop confidence in dealing with starship operations and possible problems. Actions and reactions can be reviewed, replicated, and critiqued any number of times without damage or danger.

Each student stands watches at each station and will rotate through every station in USS NEVERSAIL (NCC–0000). This policy ensures a minimum level of exposure to the varied situations present on modern Starfleet vessels.

Students must perform at a satisfactory level at every station aboard USS NEVERSAIL (NCC–0000) before embarking on the Midshipman Training Cruise. This facility is available outside of normal class hours for individuals who wish to gain additional experience in the simulators.

# TRAINING CRUISE

An integral part of Starfleet Academy Basic Program is the Midshipman Training Cruise. In the third semester of the fourth year of studies, each Midshipman goes aboard the Academy's Training Vessel for a 100 day cruise. The student is assigned to a department commensurate with the individual's selected major, placed into duty rotation with the regular crew, and fulfills the watch standing requirements of a Starfleet officer. Based on the recommendations of the student's department head, or upon request by the Midshipman, assignment to other positions aboard the Training Vessel during the cruise is possible.

Each Academy has its own Training Vessel, which is homeported at that particular Academy. To accommodate assignment of Midshipmen to the Training Cruise, each Training Vessel normally operates with a reduced manning level and is, therefore, not considered as part of the respective Fleet's operating forces. Should circumstance dictate, however, the Training Vessel and its predominately Midshipman crew may be transferred to the operational fleet. This has occurred only once in the history of Starfleet, when the Training Vessel USS ENTERPRISE (NCC–1701) was activated during the V'Ger Incident. Training Vessel assignments are:

| Academy | Ship Name | Ship Type |
|---|---|---|
| Home Fleet | USS UNIFICATION (NCC–2140) | Dreadnought |
| First Fleet | USS WILDFIRE (NCC–2027) | Command Cruiser |
| Second Fleet | USS PROCYON (NCC–1756) | Heavy Cruiser |
| Third Fleet | USS ZAHN (NCC–8606) | Battle Cruiser |
| Fourth Fleet | USS BENNINGTON (NCC–1978) | Through–deck Cruiser |

The ship's operating schedule is promulgated at least one academic year in advance, which allows the Training Vessel to transport cargo and passengers from port to port. The request for transportation of cargo or passengers is made to the ship itself, which coordinates scheduling loading, unloading, cargo space assignments, and passenger accommodations.

Several ports of call are scheduled during the Midshipman Training Cruise to allow Midshipmen and the vessel's crew to avail them selves of recreational opportunities. During one recent Midshipman Training Cruise aboard USS ZAHN (NCC–8606), the Training Vessel for Starfleet Academy (Third Fleet), the ship and crew visited Daran VI, Memory Alpha, Acadia, Camus II, and Halka III, spending an average of four days in each port.

# ADVANCED COLLEGES

## GENERAL INFORMATION

The Master of Science and the Doctor of Philosophy programs at Starfleet Academy offer graduate and post–graduate degrees in the following colleges:

- Engineering
- Fleet Operations
- Life Sciences
- Medicine
- Physical Sciences
- Social Sciences
- Space Sciences

Available majors in each College are listed elsewhere in this Handbook.

## APPLICATIONS

Applications for acceptance into an advanced degree program may be submitted at any time during an officer's Starfleet career, including Midshipmen (for a Master of Science degree). The following must be included in the application: a completed Starfleet Academy Graduate Application; a transcript from either Starfleet Academy or another accredited institution showing evidence of a Bachelor of Science (or equivalent) for the Master of Science program, or a Master of Science (or equivalent) for the Doctor of Philosophy program; and a recommendation from the applicant's commanding officer (the Dean of the College of Fleet Operations in the case of a Midshipman applying for a Master of Science degree program). For information concerning the Bachelor of Science—Doctor of Philosophy track, contact the Dean of the appropriate College.

Once the application is received by Starfleet Academy it is sent, along with supporting documentation, to an Advanced Education Admissions Committee. This Admissions Committee will review the application and, based upon this review, recommend acceptance or non–acceptance of the application. A simple majority of Committee members must agree before the applicant can be accepted into a degree program.

Should the application be rejected, the Admissions Committee will prepare a letter outlining the reasons for non–acceptance and include a recommended course of action for the individual to rectify any problem areas uncovered in the admissions process.

The individual may reapply at any time for readmission, but must specifically address how those areas delineated in the Committee's report have been satisfied.

Following acceptance, the prospective student (in collaboration with an assigned faculty mentor) must develop a Program of Studies which outlines the specific courses planned to satisfy the requirements for the degree, as well as how any course prerequisites will be satisfied. This Program of Studies is submitted to a Program Committee made up of five faculty members who are charged with the responsibility to guide the student through the academic process. Once accepted by the student's Program Committee, the student may begin classes.

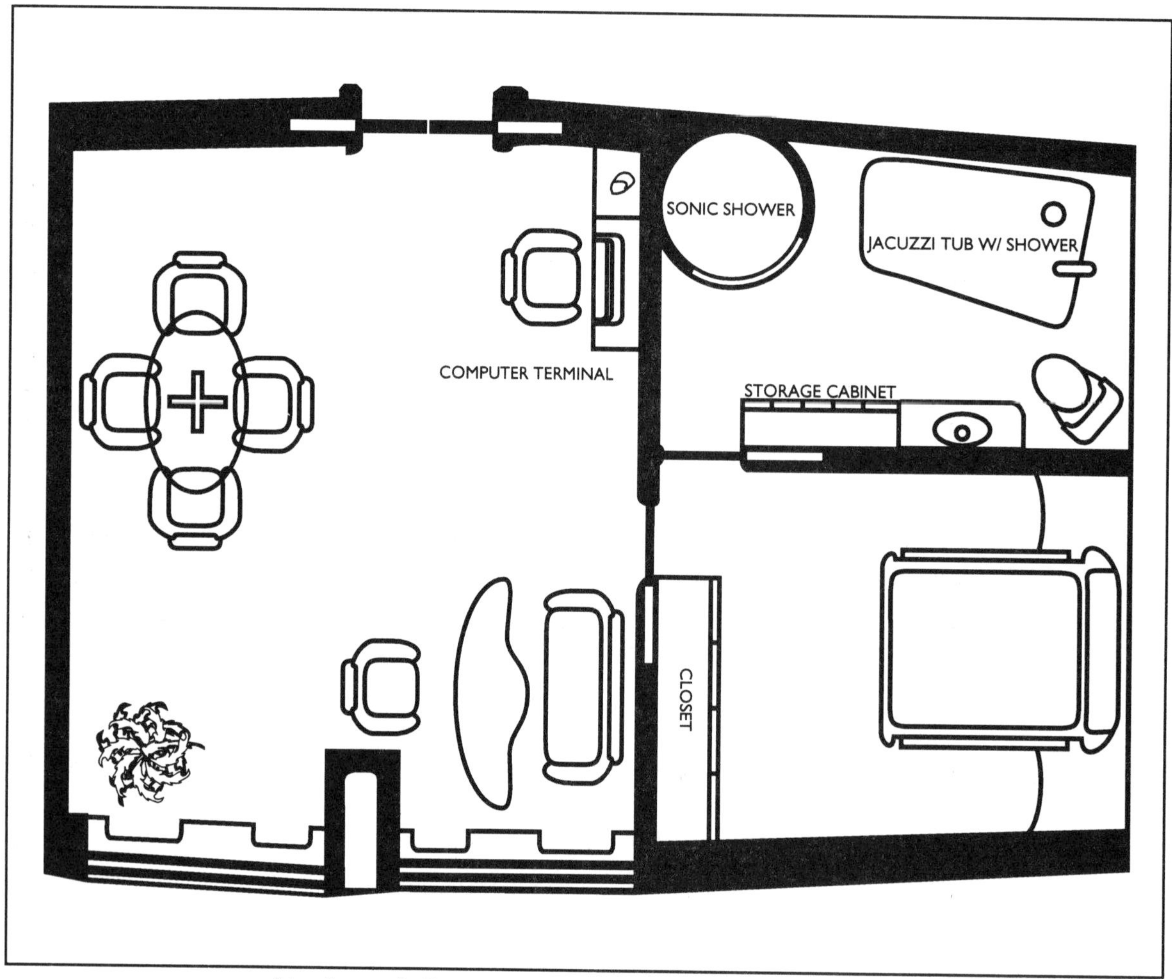


Lieutenant Commander and Below Stateroom

# UNIFORMS

The usual uniform of the day for Starfleet officers attending the Academy is either the Standard Duty Uniform Option 1 or, for females, the Standard Duty Uniform Option 2 is permitted. Depending upon planetary climate, appropriate civilian clothing is permissible during non–class hours.

Starfleet Academy is a high–visibility command and, as such, is often visited by high–ranking officials of Starfleet, the United Federation of Planets, and member worlds. Each officer must maintain a Ceremonial Dress uniform (including awards and medals) for use when appropriate.

# LIVING QUARTERS

Officers returning to Starfleet Academy for programs in one of the Advanced Colleges are provided single–occupancy quarters in one of the Residence Hulls. Each stateroom consists of a living area, a sleeping area, and sanitary facilities.

The main entrance is through a door which is either voice activated or responds automatically to the occupant's proximity (as determined by the occupant). If desired, the door may be programmed to recognize and automatically admit other individuals at the occupant's discretion.

Living quarters contain a dining table for four, a computer terminal and desk, and various items of furniture. Wide latitude is allowed officers in decorating and furnishing these quarters. Additional furnishings are available from the Academy Quartermaster. A large window on the exterior bulkhead provides a view of the campus.

The sleeping area contains a large bed with storage spaces on either side as well as above the mirrored headboard. A walk–in closet provides ample room for clothing.

The head, which is reached from the sleeping area, contains a sonic shower and a Jacuzzi tub. Additional storage facilities are located underneath the sink cabinet.

# PROMOTIONS

Starfleet officers attending Starfleet Academy maintain their eligibility for promotion in the same manner as their contemporaries at other duty stations. However, because Starfleet Academy has no Student Manning Document and consequently, no billets to become vacant, some modification to normal promotion procedures (as outlined in the Starfleet Personnel Manual) is necessary.

Each officer's performance is evaluated at the end of every semester. The individual's level of performance is compared with others in the same grade and a ranked listing is prepared. The top five percent of each listing is recommended for promotion.

These recommendations are forwarded to the individual's commanding officer for endorsement. The names of all officers who receive a recommendation from Starfleet Academy and a favorable endorsement by their commanding officer are forwarded to Starfleet Command for action.

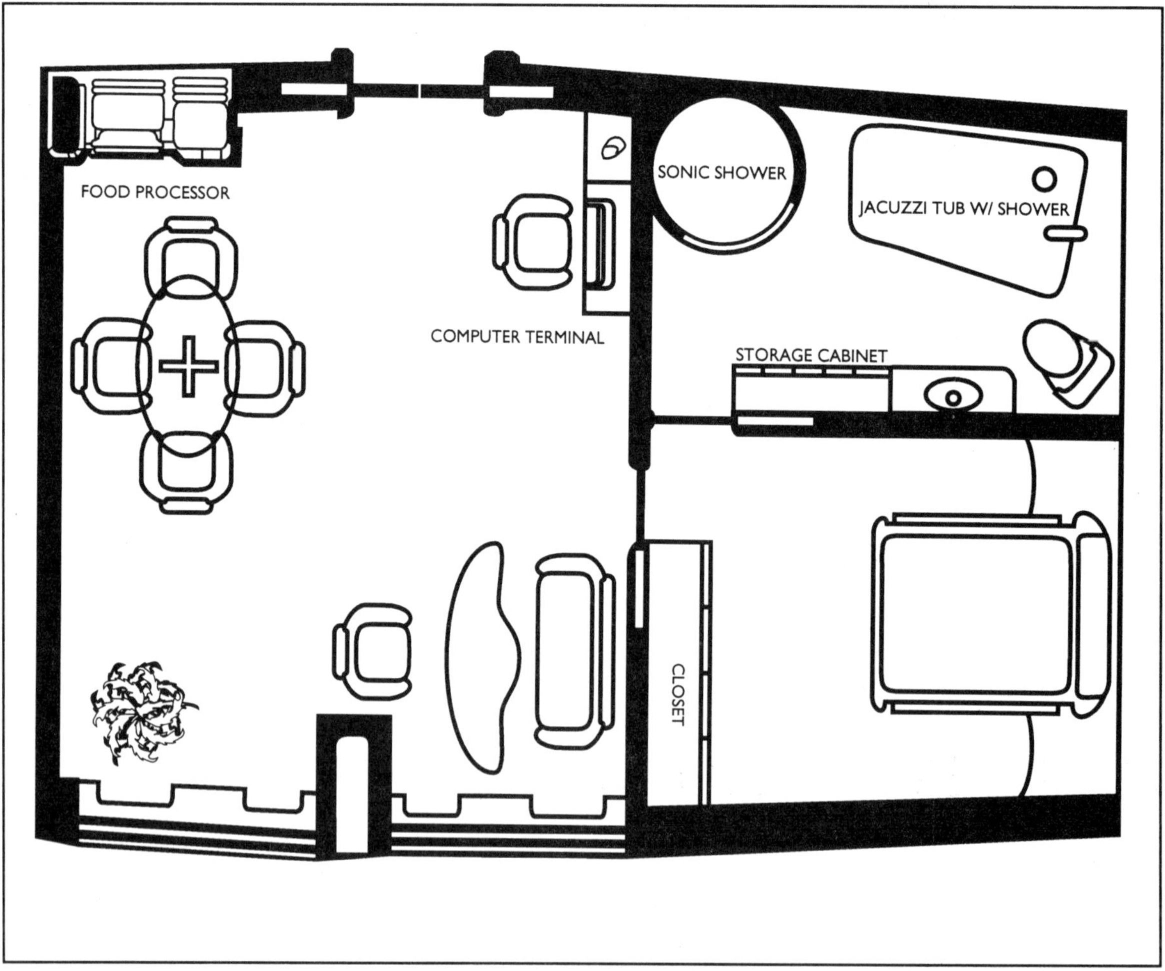


**Commander and Above Stateroom**

In no case will the names of those recommended for promotion be made public Likewise, the contents of the commanding officer's endorsement are never released.

An officer can be promoted only once during each time at Starfleet Academy, but may be considered and/or recommended for promotion at the end of each semester in attendance.

# LEAVE AND LIBERTY

Leave and liberty for Starfleet officers attending the Academy follow the same regulations applicable to Midshipmen. Leave is accrued as though the officer were attached to a normal duty station (for further information, refer to the Starfleet Personnel Manual).

# CLASS SCHEDULES

The academic year is 400 days in length. It is divided into four semesters of 100 days each. Students will attend classes from 0700 to 1650 each day for eight days. Following the last class on the eighth day, students will have two days off for rest and relaxation.

The final 10–day period of a semester is available for students to take accumulated leave or receive visitors.

During class days, a two–hour period is provided for the mid–day meal, from 1100 to 1300. The following is the class schedule:

| | |
|---|---|
| 0700–0850 | Class |
| 0900–1050 | Class |
| 1100–1300 | Lunch |
| 1300–1450 | Class |
| 1500–1650 | Class |

# MASTER OF SCIENCE (MS)

The Master of Science program is designed to increase the student's expertise in a particular field at a level exceeding the expectations of a Bachelor of Science degree. The student may select one of the majors listed in the Degree Offering section for the appropriate College or, with the approval of a faculty mentor and the Dean of the College, devise a customized program which addresses a particular area of interest to the student.

Each Master of Science degree program is composed of two distinct elements: course work and a practicum. A minimum of 16 courses at the 500 level (beyond the Bachelor of Science) selected from the Academy's curriculum in the student's major area must be completed. The practicum is designed to allow the student to complete a significant project or line of investigation with one of the corporate sponsors listed elsewhere in this Handbook. The length of the practicum varies with the major and with the project or line of investigation chosen by the student.

Following this practicum, the student must prepare and present a detailed report or thesis which addresses the project or line of investigation, including the original research plan, a detailed report of the student's activities and discoveries, what ramifications may evolve from any discoveries, and possible future related areas for investigation by others.

When all course work is completed and the practicum thesis is accepted by the student's Program Committee and the Dean of the specific College, the student will receive an appropriate diploma and be returned (in most cases) to the duty station from which transferred. For information on graduation, see the appropriate section in this Handbook.

# DOCTOR OF PHILOSOPHY (PHD)

The Doctor of Philosophy is an advanced degree which represents broad scholarly attainment; a deep grasp of a specific field of study; and expertise in conceiving, conducting, and reporting of individual research. The student is expected to display a level of intellectual growth which represents the professional stature denoted by the doctoral degree.

Each Doctor of Philosophy degree program is composed of two distinct elements: course work and a dissertation. A minimum of 16 courses at the 600 level (beyond the Master of Science) selected from the Academy's curriculum in the student's major area must be completed.

Once the course work has been completed, the student must prepare a dissertation proposal outlining a plan to demonstrate both ability to do independent research and competence in scholarly exposition. It should present original investigation, at an advanced level, of a significant problem and should provide the basis for a publishable contribution to the research literature of the major field. In most cases, the research will be accomplished in conjunction with one of the corporate sponsors listed elsewhere in this Handbook.

When all course work is completed and the dissertation is accepted by the student's Program Committee and the Dean of the specific College, the student will receive an appropriate diploma and be returned (in most cases) to the duty station from which transferred. For information on graduation, see the appropriate section in this Handbook.

# DEGREE OFFERINGS

## College of Engineering

| Major | MS | PhD |
|---|---|---|
| Aeronautics | X | |
| Architecture | X | |
| Chemical Engineering | X | X |
| Civil Engineering | X | X |
| Computer Engineering | X | X |
| Construction Engineering | X | |
| Electrical Engineering | X | X |
| Engineering | | X |
| Engineering Science | | X |
| Engineering Technology | X | X |
| Environmental Design | X | |
| Holography | X | |
| Impulse Drive Systems | X | X |
| Industrial Engineering | X | X |
| Mechanical Engineering | X | X |
| Metallurgy | X | |
| Mining | X | |

| Major | MS | PhD |
|---|---|---|
| Reclamation Technology | X | |
| Remote Sensing Packages | X | X |
| Replication Systems | X | X |
| Starship Construction | X | X |
| Starbase Construction | X | X |
| Starship Design | X | X |
| Warp Drive Dynamics | X | X |

## College of Fleet Operations

| Major | MS | PhD |
|---|---|---|
| Command, Control, and Communications ($C^3$) | X | X |
| Command | X | X |
| Communications | X | X |
| Control | X | X |
| Diplomacy | X | X |
| Fleet Operations | X | X |
| Intelligence* | X | X |
| Logistics | X | X |
| Operational Administration | | X |
| Strategy and Tactics | X | X |

*Available only to Starfleet Intelligence officers.

# College of Life Sciences

| Major | MS | PhD |
|---|---|---|
| Agriculture | X | |
| Animal Sciences | X | |
| Bacteriology | X | X |
| Biochemistry | X | X |
| Biology | X | X |
| Biophysics | X | X |
| Biotechnology | | X |
| Botany | X | X |
| Cell Biology | X | |
| Cytology | X | |
| Ecology | X | X |
| Entomology | X | |
| Environmental Sciences | X | X |
| Genetics | X | X |
| Hexapodology | X | |
| Horticulture | X | |
| Hydroponics | X | |
| Ichthyology | X | |
| Life Sciences | X | X |
| Marine Biology | X | |
| Marine Science | | X |
| Microbiology | X | |

| Major | MS | PhD |
|---|---|---|
| Molecular Biology | X | |
| Mycology | X | |
| Natural Resources Management | X | X |
| Ornithology | X | |
| Paleontology | X | |
| Pathology | X | |
| Plant Genetics | X | |
| Plant Pathology | X | |
| Plant Pharmacology | X | X |
| Plant Physiology | X | |
| Resource Management | X | X |
| Soil Science | X | |
| Zoology | X | |

## College of Medicine

| Major | MS | MD |
|---|---|---|
| Allergies | | X |
| Audiology | | X |
| Cardiology | | X |
| Chiropractic | | X |
| Dentistry | | X |
| Dermatology | | X |
| Dietetics | | X |

| Major | MS | MD |
|---|---|---|
| Emergency/Disaster Services | | X |
| Gerontology | | X |
| Gynecology | | X |
| Health Sciences | | X |
| Internal Medicine | | X |
| Medical Technology | | X |
| Medicine | | X |
| Neurology | | X |
| Nursing | X* | X** |
| Obstetrics | | X |
| Occupational Therapy | | X |
| Ophthalmology | | X |
| Optometry | | X |
| Pathology | | X |
| Pharmaceutics | | X |
| Physical Therapy | X | X |
| Podiatry | | X |
| Surgery | | X |

*Graduates will be designated a Clinical Nurse Specialist.
**Graduates will receive a PhD.

# College of Physical Sciences

| Major | MS | PhD |
|---|---|---|
| Analytical Chemistry | X | |
| Cartography | X | X |

| Major | MS | PhD |
|---|---|---|
| Chemistry | X | X |
| Computer Programming | X | X |
| Computer Science | | X |
| Cybernetics | X | |
| Ecology | X | X |
| Electron Physics | X | X |
| Elementary Particle Physics | X | X |
| Fluids and Plasmas | X | X |
| Geology | X | X |
| Hydrology | X | X |
| Information Sciences | X | X |
| Information Systems | | X |
| Inorganic Chemistry | X | X |
| Mathematics | X | X |
| Meteorology | X | |
| Molecular Physics | X | X |
| Oceanography | X | X |
| Optics | X | |
| Organic Chemistry | X | X |
| Physical Chemistry | X | X |
| Physical Science | | X |
| Physics | X | X |
| Planetary Sciences | X | X |
| Robotics | X | X |

| Major | MS | PhD |
|---|---|---|
| Solid State Physics | X | |
| Systems Analysis | X | X |
| Terraforming | X | X |

# College of Social Sciences

| Major | MS | PhD |
|---|---|---|
| Administration | X | |
| Anthropology | X | X |
| Archeology | X | X |
| Criminology | X | |
| Economics | X | X |
| Education | X | X |
| Finance | X | X |
| Fine Arts | X | X |
| Geography | X | X |
| History | X | X |
| Humanities | X | X |
| Intercultural Relations | X | X |
| Interstellar Development | X | X |
| Journalism | X | |
| Law | X* | |
| Linguistics | X | X |
| Management | X | |

| Major | MS | PhD |
|---|---|---|
| Music | X | |
| Personnel Management | X | |
| Philosophy | X | X |
| Political Science | X | X |
| Psychology | X | X |
| Recreation | X | |
| Religions | X | X |
| Social Sciences | X | X |
| Sociology | X | X |
| Visual and Performing Arts | X | |

* Juris Doctorate (JD) awarded.

## College of Space Sciences

| Major | MS | PhD |
|---|---|---|
| Astronomy | X | X |
| Astrophysics | X | X |
| Cosmology | X | X |
| Planetology | X | X |
| Space Sciences | X | X |

Wall of Memories

# CORPORATE SPONSORS

The following organizations provide internships and work study programs for Starfleet Academy students at the locations specified and for the Advanced Colleges indicated:

| Company | Location | Applicable College |
|---|---|---|
| Aa IOU Gienger | Chalna | Life Sciences |
| Abou–Ghazala Ltd. | Cairo, Earth | Space Sciences |
| Aerospatiale | Rousseau, Mars | Space Sciences |
| Ag Murpeth | Surak, Vulcan | Physical Sciences |
| Agusta Ansadado, Inc. | Fuzes, Venus | Physical Sciences<br>Social Sciences |
| Alto/Sekkulen I.F.D. | Tiber Basin, Mars | Physical Sciences |
| Animation Ultragraphics | Arrival, Tellar | Social Sciences |
| Aris Mastac | Prime Dockyards, Daran V | Engineering |
| Arkararata Government Consortium | Elevendin, Edos | Social Sciences |
| Asakaze Ordnance Systems, Ltd. | Honshu–Hamamatsu, Earth | Engineering |
| Avondale Group | Cygnet XIV | Social Sciences |
| Avondale Group | New Dallas, Rigel IV | Social Sciences |
| A'Alakon Landiss Inc | Divallax, Andor | Engineering<br>Physical Sciences |
| Bank of Andor | Daldorran, Andor | Social Sciences |
| Baxter Pharmaceuticals, Inc. | Chicago, Earth | Medical<br>Life Sciences |
| Benkhulen Systems | Singapore, Earth | Engineering |

| Company | Location | Applicable College |
|---|---|---|
| Bio–Genetic Research, Inc. | Rousseau, Mars | Life Sciences<br>Medical |
| Bzevhistakis Kor Conglessum | Bortis, Tellar | Social Sciences |
| $CH^2M$ Hill | Ennan VI | Life Sciences |
| Chandley Works, Ltd. | Caravalla, Mars | Engineering |
| Charlotte's Shields, Inc. | Quiberon Prime, Alpha Centauri | Engineering<br>Physical Sciences |
| Chiokis Starship Construction | Thelavor, Andor | Engineering<br>Physical Sciences |
| Cochrane Warp Dynamics | Minos al Rijil, Alpha Centauri VII | Engineering<br>Physical Sciences |
| Cosmadyne Corporation | Boston, Earth | Engineering<br>Physical Sciences |
| Cosmadyne Corporation | Houston, Earth | Engineering<br>Physical Sciences<br>Social Sciences |
| Crystobal SM/S | Manila, Earth | Social Sciences |
| Daystrom Data Concepts | San Francisco, Earth | Engineering<br>Physical Sciences |
| Daystrom Computer Systems, Inc. | Lunaport, Luna (Sol IIIA) | Engineering<br>Physical Sciences |
| Dennison/Westinghouse Hyperphotic Propulsion Division | San Francisco, Earth | Engineering<br>Physical Sciences<br>Social Sciences |
| Durasport, Inc. | Ursinnis, Argelius | Social Sciences |
| Empress Spacecraft Design and Building | Port Copernicus, Luna (Sol IIIA) | Engineering |

| Company | Location | Applicable College |
|---|---|---|
| Eristaffe–Zynn Space Systems | Sebaldhasta, Deneb V | Engineering<br>Physical Sciences |
| ETNetc | Hurada III | Life Sciences |
| Farranti Mnemonics | Berkshire, Earth | Engineering<br>Physical Sciences |
| General Entertainment Concepts | New Orleans, Earth | Social Sciences |
| Ggramphud Histo–Cryogenics, Inc. | Tellar | Medicine<br>Physical Sciences |
| Hibeam Energies, Ltd. | Luna City, Luna (Sol IIIA) | Engineering<br>Physical Sciences |
| Hycor | Woburn, Earth | Engineering |
| Illifi/Paruge | Aranab Tretos, Delta IV | Fleet Operations |
| Interstellar Business Machines | Chicago, Earth | Social Sciences |
| Ishikawajima Harima Industries | Yokohama, Earth | Engineering<br>Physical Sciences |
| Jacar Jafra Enterprises | Wolf 359 X | Life Sciences |
| Jullundur–Lahore, Ltd. | Bombay, Earth | Engineering<br>Physical Sciences |
| Kal Achal Conglessum | Takuv, Tellar | Social Sciences |
| Keindoffer–Klaatsen DSC | Munich, Earth | Social Sciences<br>Fleet Operations |
| Klorati Drives | Tellar | Engineering<br>Physical Sciences |
| Kuchata Pratus Ikyla | Arrasta, Daran V | Space Sciences |
| Kym Lan Den Earth | New Kyoto, Earth | Space Sciences |

| Company | Location | Applicable College |
| --- | --- | --- |
| Leeding Engines, Ltd. | Sydney, Earth | Engineering<br>Physical Sciences |
| Leeper–Fell Universial, Ltd. | Tritium, Mars | Social Sciences<br>Engineering<br>Physical Sciences |
| Litton–Sedeco Shipbuilding | Pearl Harbor, Earth | Engineering<br>Physical Sciences |
| Lockheed Associated Industries | Seattle, Earth | Engineering<br>Physical Sciences |
| Loraxial Corporation | Andor | Engineering<br>Physical Sciences |
| Mandor Industries, Ltd. | Dalhalam, Delta IV | Space Sciences |
| Marsfoods Corporation | Vandalia, Mars | Social Sciences |
| Monolithic Memories | Vulcan | Engineering<br>Physical Sciences |
| Morris Magtronics | Palyria, Mars | Engineering<br>Physical Sciences |
| Multiplanet Metals, Inc. | Gduray, Tellar | Physical Sciences |
| M'Yengh Yards | Shzerensohr, Cait | Engineering |
| Nestiri Associated Industries | Old Colony,<br>61 Cyngi A IV | Social Sciences |
| New Amsterdam Gravitics | New Amsterdam,<br>Alpha III | Engineering<br>Physical Sciences |
| Newport News Shipbuilding | Avalon, Earth | Engineering<br>Physical Sciences |
| Newport News Shipbuilding | East Bank Facility,<br>Deneb V | Engineering<br>Physical Sciences |

| Company | Location | Applicable College |
|---|---|---|
| Newport News Shipbuilding | Kin Raach, Alpha Centauri VII | Engineering<br>Physical Sciences |
| Newport News Shipbuilding Headquarters | Newport News, Earth | Engineering<br>Fleet Operations<br>Physical Sciences<br>Social Sciences |
| Nutritech Corporation, McDonald's Division | Marsport, Mars | Medical<br>Physical Sciences<br>Social Sciences |
| Orage Ijek | Aksajak, Andor | Medical |
| Pan–Galactic Productions | London, Earth | Social Sciences |
| Phoenix Enterprises Ltd. | Reynard, Salazaar | Social Sciences |
| Plessey Group | Essex, Earth | Engineering |
| Prentice–Schafer, Inc. | Marsport, Mars | Social Sciences |
| Prinzhenri S.N. | Rio de Janeiro, Earth | Social Sciences |
| Provoost Laboratories | Adelphous IV | Life Sciences |
| Raakuv | Gaziwahaida, Andor | Space Sciences |
| Racak Werft F.M.C. | Stratos, Ardana | Space Sciences |
| Rantura Shipping Lines | Daran, Deneva | Social Sciences |
| Rapier Dynamics Group | New Aberdeen, Aldebaran III | Engineering<br>Physical Sciences<br>Social Sciences |
| Rodriguez Ingenieria | Lima, Earth | Social Sciences |
| Sandia Shipbuilding and Conversion, Albuquerque Division | Albuquerque, Earth | Engineering<br>Fleet Operations<br>Physical Sciences<br>Social Sciences |

| Company | Location | Applicable College |
|---|---|---|
| Sandia Shipbuilding and Conversion, Albuquerque Division | Earth Orbit Spacedock Facilities, Earth | Engineering<br>Physical Sciences |
| Sarlis | Par Fir, Vulcan | Medical<br>Social Sciences |
| Scarbak Propulsion Systems | Cairo, Earth | Engineering<br>Physical Sciences |
| Sedona Ridge Life Sciences | Seabrook, Earth | Life Sciences |
| Selenia Sistemi S.P.A. Inc. | Rome, Earth | Space Sciences |
| Seskon Trella | Chagala, Tellar | Social Sciences |
| Shaktir Tripel | Surak, Vulcan | Medical<br>Social Sciences |
| Shiputer Corporation | Bristol, Earth | Engineering |
| Shor Ta'kel Ltd. | Central Docks, 40 Eridani | Engineering<br>Physical Sciences |
| Shuvinaaljis Warp Technologies, Inc. | Shuridar, Vulcan | Engineering<br>Physical Sciences |
| Signaal Electronic Enterprises Inc. | Mediterranea, Earth | Engineering<br>Physical Sciences |
| Skat–Rar Weapons Systems | Ezuruk, Andor | Engineering<br>Fleet Operations<br>Physical Sciences |
| Smith & Smythe Motor Works, Ltd. | Surleft, Andor | Engineering<br>Physical Sciences |
| Starwide Merchants | Grinitaine, Alpha Centauri | Social Sciences |
| Surelox Systems | Tybrenn, Arcturus | Engineering<br>Physical Sciences |

| Company | Location | Applicable College |
|---|---|---|
| Survivors Corporation | Tycho City, Deneva | Social Sciences |
| Sy Ris Abagon | New Aberdeen, Aldebaran III | Engineering |
| S'lek Varan | Shuridar, Vulcan | Engineering |
| Tachyon Micromechanics, Ltd. | Grinidasa, Arcturus | Engineering<br>Fleet Operations<br>Physical Sciences |
| Tidjikja/Atar Associated Industries | Rastaribi, Regulus | Space Sciences |
| Tlixis Ramab RRB | Balikan, Coridan III | Medical<br>Social Sciences |
| Trestis ar Trestis | Pangaear, Izar | Physical Sciences |
| Triax Medifore | Villa Carlos, Earth | Medical |
| Valdemar NCS Inc. | Copenhagen, Earth | Social Sciences |
| Vicker Engineering Group, Ltd. | Cumbria, Earth | Engineering<br>Physical Sciences |
| Vickers Shipbuilding Group, Ltd. | Arcadia Lake, Mars | Engineering |
| Vickers Shipbuilding Group, Ltd. | Cumbria Prime, Earth | Engineering |
| Vickers Shipbuilding Group, Ltd. | London, Earth | Engineering |
| Visi Un Da | Arlapida Harbor, Izar | Fleet Operations |
| Vulcan Monetary Society | Vulcan | Social Sciences |
| Wilson Energies, Ltd. | Edinburgh, Earth | Engineering<br>Physical Sciences |

| Company | Location | Applicable College |
|---|---|---|
| Zodiac Interstellar Industries | Marsport, Mars | Physical Sciences<br>Social Sciences<br>Space Sciences |

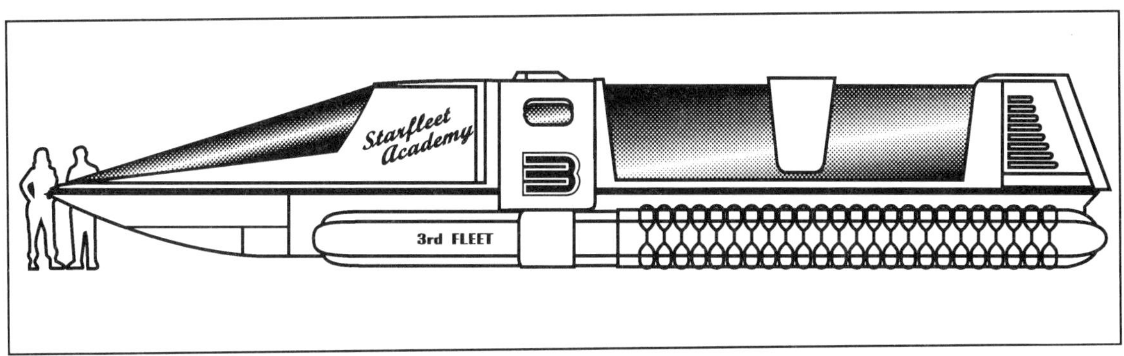


Typical Passenger Shuttle

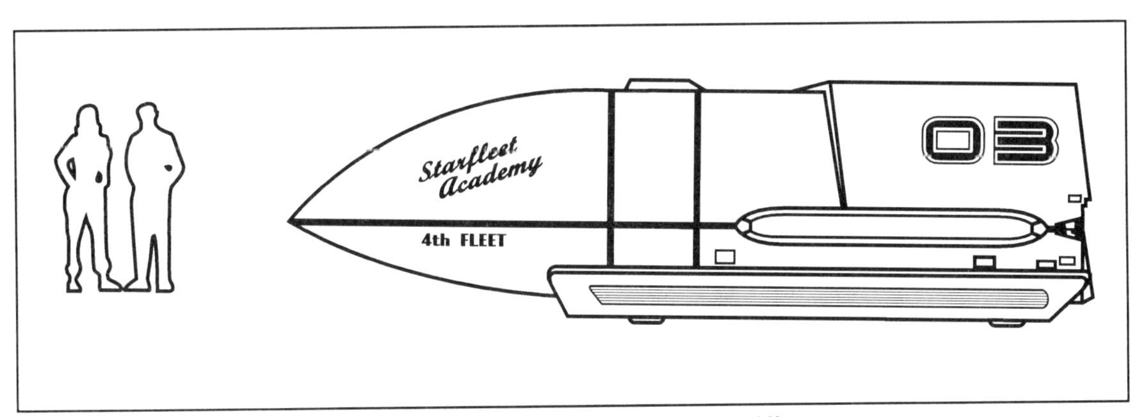


Typical Student Training Shuttle

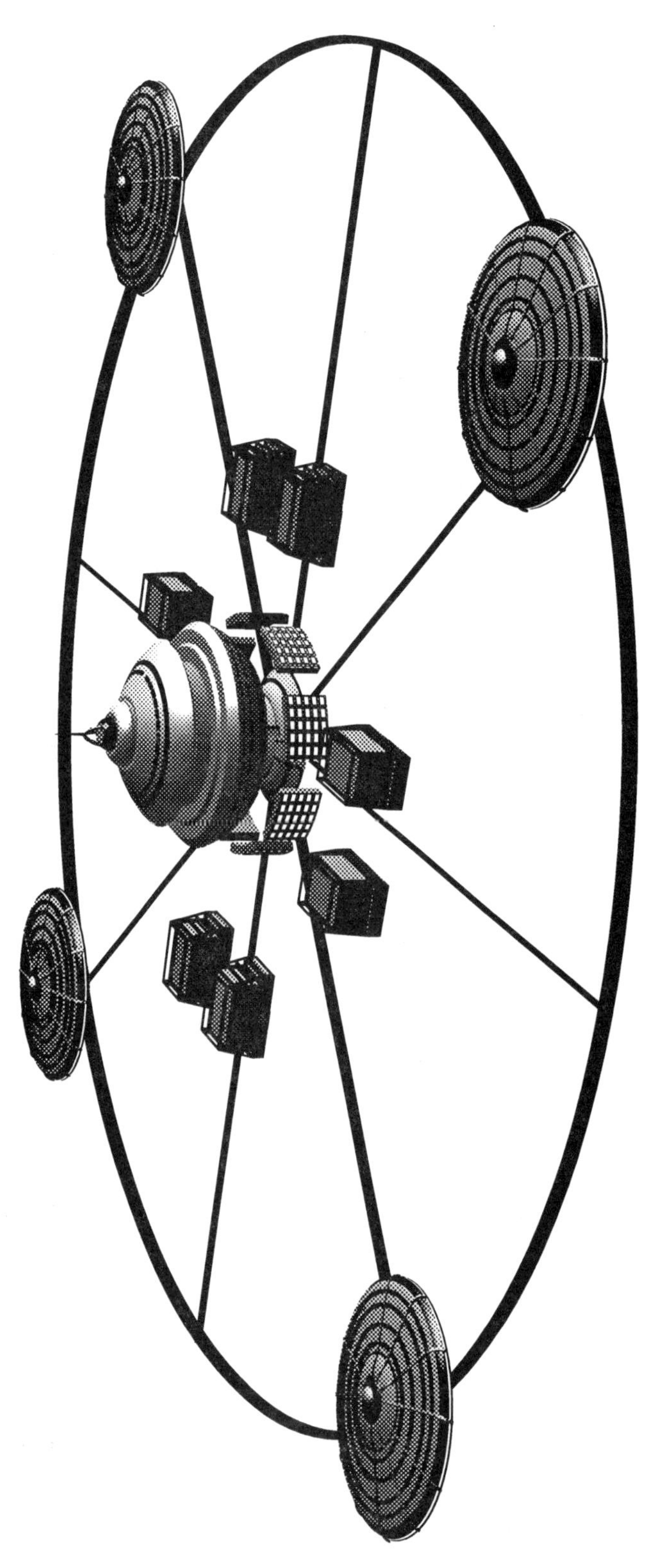

Starfleet Academy (Home Fleet)

# COURSE DESCRIPTIONS

## SFA 001—Physiological Psychology I

Advanced study of the organic variables as they relate to the behavioral process. Areas to be covered include: the nervous system and endocrine system; experimental techniques; development of the sensory process to include olfaction, somatic senses, auditon and pattern coding systems of taste. Special attention to the Reticular Theory of Perception as it relates to the control of afferent messages. Emotion theory, peripheral mechanisms of emotion, coping mechanisms and biofeedback.

## SFA 002—Physiological Psychology II

Continuation of Physiological Psychology I (SFA 001) building on the foundation laid in that course. Theory as it relates to central mechanisms to include Limbic Function, brainstem, spinal cord, Diencephalic and biochemical mechanisms. Electrical Stimulation of the Brain (ESB); interpretation involving ESB and drive states, review of the effects of mixed positive/negative effects. Drive–reduction, incentive and performed motor patterns theory as they relate to current developments in modification. An overview of cognitive functioning, integration, and functional disorders.

## SFA 008—Replicator Systems

Transporter–based molecular synthesis theory, resolution limits, memory matrix requirements, phase–transition coil chambers, quantum geometry transformational matrix fields. Replication versus storage. Data compression and averaging techniques, single–bit inaccuracies, quantum electron–state data.

## SFA 011—Principles of Systematic Biology

Systematic theory and philosophy applied to kinds, diversity, and relationships among organisms. Phrenetic, cladistic, and numerical techniques as applied to systematic studies. Levels and methods of biological classification.

## SFA 016—Physics of the Galaxy

Observations of the distribution of stars, clusters, gases, and dust in the galaxy. Theory of the equilibrium of stellar systems, Vlasov equation, Fokker–Planck equation, Jeans' Theorem, and the Third Integral. Spiral structure theory. Interstellar clouds, evolution of supernova envelopes, star formation, and the energy budget of the interstellar medium. Wormholes.

**SFA 022—Introduction to Solid–State Chemistry**

Development of relationships between electronic structure of elements, bonding characteristics, and crystal structure. Characterization of atomic and molecular arrangements in crystalline solids. Mechanisms and energy changes in chemical reactions and phase transformations. Chemical and physical properties of solids—metals, semiconductors, insulators, glasses, and polymers—as they relate to basic atomic parameters and processing technology.

**SFA 023—Law, Technology, and Public Policy**

In–depth examination of the relationship between technology and the legal system. Responses of the legal system to new social problems created by new or existing technology. Technological change in response to legal action. Changes in legal theory and practice resulting from new technical developments. Responses of the political system to proliferating technology.

**SFA 024—Herpetology**

A multi–disciplinary investigation of reptiles and amphibians. Topics include: general features, classification, form and function; adaptations, specializations, parallel and convergent evolution; anatomy, embryology and physiology; complement system characteristics; behavior, communication nodes, and biogeography.

**SFA 027—Transporter Systems**

The five–stage transporter operation. Transport chamber, operator's console, transporter controller, primary energizing coils, phase transition coils, molecular imagining scanners, pattern buffers, biofilter operation, emitter pad array, targeting scanners, static charges, auto–sequencer. Annular Confinement Beam, quark manipulation, error–checking and correction routines, Heisenberg compensators, Doppler compensation, emergency shunting and its limitations, evacuation procedures.

**SFA 030—Shipboard Sensor Systems for non–Engineers**

Panel operations, suitability, parametric limitations and interpretation of data. Course concentrates on long–range sensors, lateral sensor arrays and instrument probes. Not open to Engineering majors.

## SFA 038—Pattern Recognition and Analysis

Fundamentals of characterizing and recognizing patterns and features of interest in numerical data. Basic tools and theory for signals. Understanding problems with examples from multi–media, environmental monitoring, computer vision, remote sensing, medical and biological image processing. Decision theory, statistical classification, maximum likelihood and Bayesian estimation, non–parametric methods, unsupervised learning and clustering, context–dependent methods. Additional topics from active research.

## SFA 045—Oceanography

Water properties such as temperature, salinity, density and pressure; transmission of electrical, optical, and acoustic stimuli. The energy exchange at the air–sea surface; the general motion of seawater, including tides and the several forms of surface and subsurface waves and currents. The chemistry of seawater, including identification of dissolved constituents, chemical and biochemical cycles, geochemical models. The geological character of ocean basins, constituent rocks and marine sediments; ridges, rock magnetism, and heat flow.

## SFA 051—Cosmology

Thermal backgrounds in space. Cosmological principle and its consequences: Newtonian cosmology and types of "universes;" survey of relativistic cosmology; horizons and horizon events. Evolution in cosmology; radiation and element synthesis; physical models of the early stages. Formation of large–scale structure to variability of physical laws. First and last states.

## SFA 057—Introduction to Geology

Major rock–forming minerals, rock–forming processes, and rock types. Geologic structures and relationships observable in the field. Dating of rocks by fossil and isotopic methods. Sediment movement and landform development by moving water, winds, and ice. Crustal processes and evolution in terms of global plate tectonics.

## SFA 070—Stellar System Dynamics

Introduction to chaotic behavior in conservative systems with examples drawn primarily from the rotation and orbital dynamics of planets and satellites. Includes surfaces of section, Lyapunov exponents, perturbation theory, JAM theorem, resonances, onset of chaos, double pendulum, Henon–Heiles problems, restricted three–body problem, spin–orbit coupling, orbital resonances, adiabatic invariants, adiabatic chaos, tidal evolution, capture into resonance, stability of stellar systems.

**SFA 079—Urban Design**

The design of urban environments. Strategies for change in large areas of cities, to be developed over time, involving different actors. Fitting forms into natural, constructed, historical, and cultural outlooks; enabling desirable activity patterns; conceptualizing built form; providing infrastructure and service systems; guiding the sensory character of development.

**SFA 083—Medicolegal Investigation**

Study of the accepted definitions of death as it relates to cerebral functions. Catalog of postmortem events in determining the time of death. Identification of remains with special attention to recognition of features, clothing and personal effects, roentgenologic examination, skeletal examination, determination of sex, age, and estimate of stature. Blunt and sharp force injury, thermal effects of special weapons and a review of toxicological procedures. Selected procedures and medicological reporting as it relates to treaty protocol and convention are also examined.

**SFA 085—Selected Topics in Social Sciences**

Guest lecturers present varied topics of current interest in the field of Social Sciences. Interactive discussions of presentations/lectures/exhibits with panels of experts and/or individuals. Lectures and topics subject to change based on availability, emergent findings, and immediacy of subjects.

**SFA 089—Environmental Systems**

Atmospheric systems: plenum systems, photosynthetic bioprocessing; particulate filtration; contingency supply modules; distribution network; crossroads and return network. Gravity systems: generator networks; inertial dampening field interface; graviton field generators; waveguide conduit matrix; field bleeding. Emergency environmental support systems; contingency atmospheric and power supply; emergency shelters. Evacuation procedures.

**SFA–092—Individuals, Groups, and Organizations**

Develops basic concepts for understanding individual, group, and organizational behavior through critical analysis of important works in the field. Areas covered:

cognitive psychology, behavioral decision making, group process and performance, and organizational culture and adaptation.

### SFA 095—Biological Oceanography

Intensive overview of biological oceanography. After introductions to physical oceanography and diversity of life in the oceans, fundamental topics in population dynamics, behavioral and community ecology, population genetics, physiology and biochemistry and marine organisms. Microbiology, phytoplankton, zooplankton, biogeochemistry, sediment dynamics, benthos, and evolution.

### SFA 096—Political Development

Examines major political trends and issues in contemporary developing social/political systems, including regime changes, democratization, growth of ethnic identities and ethnic conflict, political consequences of rapid population growth, urbanization, mass communications, and diffusion of education. Problems of creating legitimate authority, process of creating and sustaining effective institutions.

### SFA 099—Federation Political Economy

Analysis of contemporary and historical issues in Federation political economy with special emphasis on public finance and economic regulation. Selected topics in trade and tax policy, agricultural, transport, labor, and environmental regulations, and local public finance treated in some detail.

### SFA 102—Selected Topics in Space Sciences

Seminar on current topics, with a different focus each class. Typical topics: gravitational lenses, active galactic nuclei, neutron stars and pulsars, galaxy formation, supernovae and supernova remnants, brown dwarfs, wormholes, temporal displacements.

### SFA 104—The Society of Mind

Introduction to a theory that tries to explain how minds are made from collections of simpler processes. Treats such aspects of thinking as vision, language, learning, reasoning, memory, consciousness, ideals, emotions, and personality. Incorporates ideas from psychology, artificial intelligence, and computer science to resolve theoretical issues.

### SFA 105—Infectious Diseases

Review of literature regarding bacterial and fungal infections, with special attention to cross–species strains. Included: Staphylococcal, Meningococcal, and Salmonella infections, Achilles Fever, Synthococcus novae. Virus infections will concentrate on Viral Hepatitis, Myxovirus infections, Toxoplasmosis, Stevena–Johnson Syndrome and Toxic Epidermal Neurolysis. Isolation techniques and evacuation considerations will be explored.

### SFA 108—Defector Shields

Navigational deflector: graviton polarity source generators; subspace field distortion amplifiers; subspace field coils. Deflectors: conformal transmission grids; Cerenkov radiation; graviton polarity source generators; subspace field distortion amplifiers; heat dissipation; transitional field interaction.

### SFA 110—Shipboard Phasers

Rapid Nadion Effect. *Fushigi–no–umi* super–conducting crystals. Firing order; thermal effects; field halos, emitter crystals; phaser–transparent hull anticorrosion coating; cooling systems; EPS submaster flow regulator; plasma distribution manifold. Activation sequence: magnetic switching gates; the phaser function command processor; prefire chambers; beam emission; force coupling; EM polarization.

### SFA 111—Starfleet Orientation I

Starfleet organization, branches, and interrelationships; purpose, mission, and goals; Starfleet's role within the UFP; categories of Starfleet officers, i.e., command, operations, science, engineering, intelligence, etc.

### SFA 112—UFP History

History and development of the United Federation of Planets beginning with predecessor governmental concepts and constructs; significant historical individuals, events and consequences; alternative futures.

### SFA 113—Physical Training I

Establishment of individual baseline physical conditioning; development of personal regime to attain idea level of physical fitness; introduction to weight lifting, aerobics, low and high impact systems, swimming, and other training techniques.

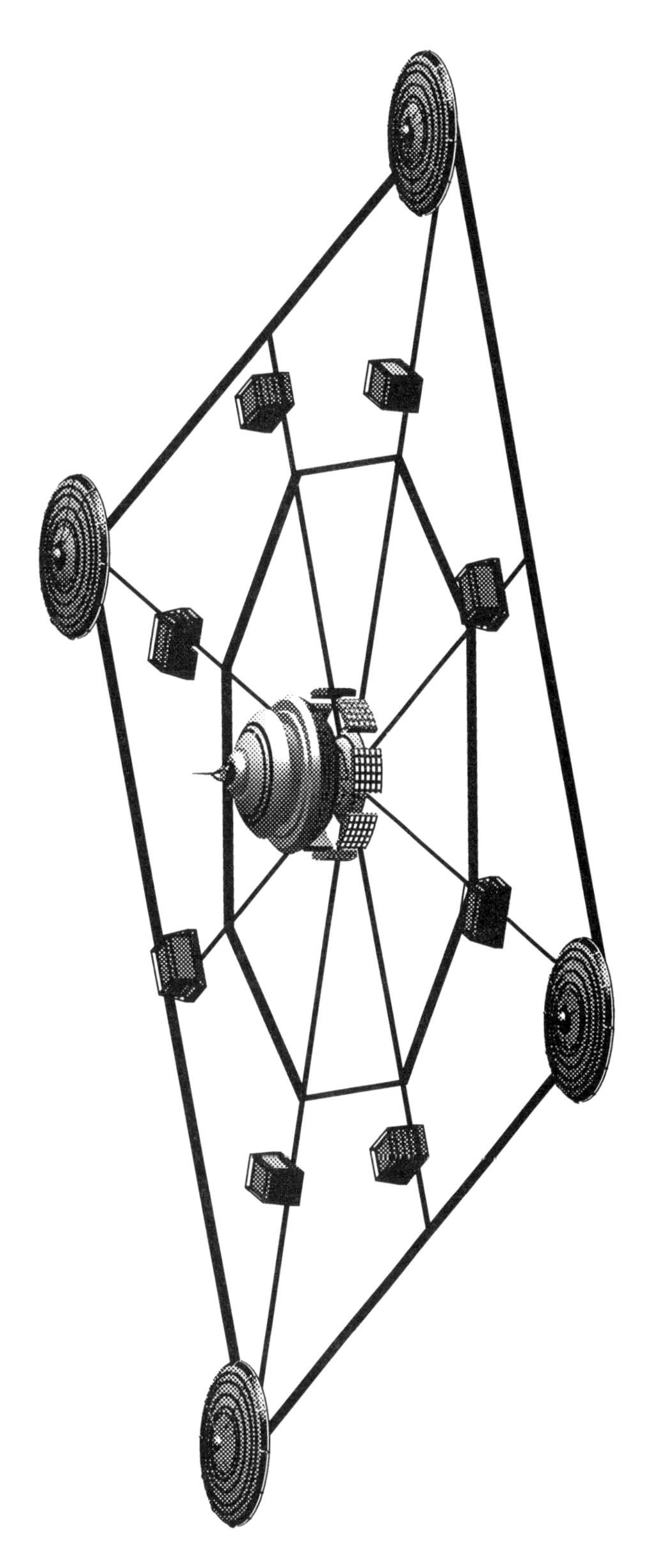

Starfleet Academy (First Fleet)

### SFA 114—Language I

Basics of language development and evolution; overview of main Federation member world languages including English, Andorian, Tellarite, etc.

### SFA 115—Computers I

Building abstractions: computational processes; higher–order procedures; compound data; data abstractions. Controlling interactions: generic operations; self–describing data; message passing; streams and infinite data structures. Meta–linguistic abstraction: interpretation of programming languages; machine model; compilation; embedded languages.

### SFA 116—Personal Combat I

Overview of personal defensive techniques including Karate, Tai Chai, jiu–jisu, Capoeira, Shootfighing, Penhtjak Silat, Ninjitsu, and others.

### SFA 117—Artistic Expression I

Designed to acquaint the student with various means and methods of self–expression through visual and auditory mediums; investigation of poetry, literature, and music. Special projects available for the student in collaboration with faculty mentors.

### SFA 121—Starfleet Orientation II

Continuation of Starfleet Orientation I (SFA 111) building upon the foundation laid in that course. A career in Starfleet; options; typical career paths; benefits and responsibilities; retirement.

### SFA 122—Military Science I

The basics: organization for combat; the 5–paragraph Operational Order; principles of communication; defilade considerations; 3V offensive concept; analysis of the combat situation; small unit tactics in offensive and defensive scenarios; analysis of selected encounters. Extensive use of holodeck simulations and field exercises.

## SFA 123—Physical Training II

Continuation of Physical Training I (SFA 113) building upon the foundation laid in that course. Implementation of physical fitness regime previously developed; evaluation of program and plan modifications as necessary.

## SFA 124—Language II

Continuation of Language I (SFA 114) building upon the foundation laid in that course. Overview of main non–Federation languages including Ferengi, Romulan, Gorn, etc.

## SFA 125—Computers II

Continuation of Computers I (SFA 115) and building upon the foundations lain in that course. Architecture of digital systems, emphasizing structural principles common to a wide range of technologies. Multilevel implementation strategies; definition of primitives and their mechanization using lover–level elements. Analysis of potential concurrency; precedence constraints and performance measures; pipelined and multidimensional systems. Instruction set design issues.

## SFA 126—Personal Combat II

Continuation of Personal Combat I (SFA 116) building upon the foundation lain in that course. In–depth study of personal defensive techniques.

## SFA 127—Artistic Expression II

Continuation of Artistic Expression II (SFA 117) and building upon the foundation lain in that course. Sculpture in various mediums, painting, holographic images. Special projects available for the student in collaboration with faculty mentors.

## SFA 131—First Aid

From basic first aid to advanced. The general principles of first aid and life–supporting concepts for humanoids and non–humanoids. Taught with a combination of classroom and holodeck simulations. Topics include: cardiac functions, cardiopulmonary resuscitation, massive trauma, field surgical procedures, combat triage, death and dying, alternative methods of healing. The Ultimate Choice. Exposure, bites and stings, bleeding, amputation, biological and chemical hazards exposure.

**SFA 132—Physical Training III**

Continuation of Physical Training II (SFA 123) building upon the foundation laid in that course. Implementation of physical fitness regime previously developed; evaluation of program and plan modifications as necessary.

**SFA 133—Nonlinear Dynamics and Chaos**

Introduction to nonlinear dynamics, with applications. Emphasizes analytical methods, examples, and geometric thinking. Topics: bifurcations, phase plane. Nonlinear oscillators: pendulum, phase model, van der Pol, Duffing. Perturbation and averaging theory. Nonlinear phenomena: hysteresis and phase–locking. Coupled oscillators in biology and physics. Center maniform theory. Chaos: Lorenz model, iterated mappings, period doubling, renormalization.

**SFA 134—Personal Combat III**

Continuation of Personal Combat II (SFA 126) building upon the foundation laid in that course. Individual practice of personal defensive techniques chosen by the student.

**SFA 135—Military Science II**

Continuation of Military Science I (SFA 122) building upon the foundations laid in that course. The Big Picture: command and staff organization; mission types, considerations, and inherent difficulties; the role and utilization of military intelligence; logistics as a crucial factor; strategies of Federation and non–Federation forces; analysis of selected encounters; Game Theory. Extensive use of holodeck simulations and field exercises.

**SFA 136—Computers III**

Continuation of Computers II (SFA 125) and building upon the foundations laid in that course. Applications of search, constraint propagation, rule chaining, frame inheritance, and other high–level, problem–solving techniques in expert systems, robotics, and natural–language understanding. Regularity–based, explanation–based, and neural net learning. Symbolic and nonsymbolic approaches to sensing, reaction, and manipulation in complicated environments.

### SFA 137—Photon Torpedoes

Torpedo configuration: casing components; holding tanks; central combiner tank; magnetic suspension components; target acquisition; guidance and detonation assemblies. Sequential field induction coils; launch assist gas generators; flash sterilization. Other applications.

### SFA 138—Emergency Medicine

Introduction to basic and advanced life–support measures. Review of the circulatory system of humanoids and non–humanoids with techniques utilized in intravenous therapy and collection of laboratory specimens. Cardiac and pulmonary, neurologic, metabolic, toxicological, environmental, genitourinary emergencies. Wound management with special attention given to skull, spinal cord, facial, eye, ear, nose, throat, chest, abdominal, limb, burn trauma, and multiple trauma cases.

### SFA 139—Bioenergetics

Cellular biochemical components and metabolism, regulation and control of intermediary metabolism; metabolic pathways associated with biological energy production, electron transport in choroplasts and mitochrondra biosynthesis of ATP and other like substances in both humanoid and non–humanoids.

### SFA 141—Communications

Communication systems in Starfleet and commercial systems and interfacing. Buoy systems, point–of–origin translators, routing concepts, Universal Translator, EPSILON–class Communication stations; listening posts. Wave propagation, intelligence loading, communication devices, security, interloping.

### SFA 142—Physical Training IV

Continuation of Physical Training III (SFA 132) building upon the foundation laid in that course. Implementation of physical fitness regime previously developed; evaluation of program and plan modifications as necessary.

### SFA 143—Complexity Theory

Nondeterministic, alternating, probabilistic, and parallel computation models. Boolean circuits. Complexity classes and complete sets. The polynomial–time hierarchy. Interactive proof systems. Relativization. Definitions of randomness. Interactive proof systems and probabilistically checkable proofs. Approaches in the P=NP? and related questions.

**SFA 144—Personal Combat IV**

Continuation of Personal Combat III (SFA 126) building upon the foundation laid in that course. Individual practice and personal defensive technique chosen by the student.

**SFA 145—Away Team Operations**

The six types of way teams: medical, diplomatic, survey, security, research, and Search and Rescue. Their purposes, composition, cautions and consideration; execution and appropriate reporting procedures. Extensive use of holodeck scenarios.

**SFA 146—Computers IV**

Continuation of Computers III (SFA 136) and building upon the foundation laid in that course. Modern system theory with applications to control, signal processing, related areas. Topics: least–norm and recursive least–square–error solutions; state space models of discrete– and continuous–time, multi–input/output systems; linear time–invariant systems; controllability, observability, modes, minimality, transfer function matrices, compensators, state feedback, optimal regulation, observers; nonlinear systems and optimal control

**SFA 147—Psychotherapy**

General principles of psychotherapy to include objectives and approaches, extra therapeutic (non–specific) healing aids, supportive therapy, reductive therapy, and the selective versus supportive, reductive, and reconstructive approaches. Initial interview and diagnosis, problem evaluation and estimate of prognosis. General review of adjunctive aids in psychotherapy will include relaxation and meditation, somatic therapy, anti–depressant and anti–anxiety drugs, doses of psychotropic drugs, and hypnosis.

**SFA 150—Art as Meaning and Technique**

Philosophical analysis of various arts, with an emphasis on the ways in which they both create and communicate meaning through techniques that define their formal structure. Particular focus on aesthetic problems about the expression of feeling and cognition.

## SFA 155—Introduction to Botany

Overview of plant anatomy, physiology, classification, evolution and ecology, covering both higher and lower plants. Interaction of planets with their environment, including plant–water relationships, carbon gain and utilization and soil mineral nutrition.

## SFA 161—Reaction Control Systems

Gas–fusion reaction chamber; magneto–hydrodynamic energy field trap; upper and lower vectored–thrust exhaust nozzles. Fuel transfer: magnetic–peristaltic pumps; pressure regulators; distributive nodes; step–up plasma compression generator; standard capacitance taps; field traps. Precision mooring beam tractor emitters.

## SFA 163—Engineering Operations and Safety

Operational concepts and safety considerations in the field of starship engineering. Mean–Time–Between–Failure concepts; preventive maintenance; emergency shut–down procedures; catastrophic emergency procedures; cytoprotective garments; tele–operations; extravehicular suits; jettison procedures.

## SFA 164—Remote Sensing Packages

Long–range sensors: wide– and narrow–angle active EM scanners; gamma ray telescope; EM flux sensor; life form analysis cluster; field stress sensor; gravimetric distortion scanner; neutrino imaging scanner; thermal imaging. Navigational sensors: Quasar telescope; wide– and narrow–angle IR source trackers; multi–beacon receivers; graviton detectors; particle detectors; cartographic processor; time–base beacon receiver; coordinate imager. Lateral sensor array. Instrument probes. Tricorders.

## SFA 165—Principles of Axiomatic Design

Introduction to design and design processes; introduction to design axioms, corollaries, and theorems; mathematical representation of design; formulation of design matrix; analysis of functional independence; graphical representation of functional independence; measure of information content; application to process planning; case studies involving real problems; use of predicate logic and prolog in axiomatic design.

## SFA 179—Essentials of Planetary Science

Fundamental physical concepts pertaining to the study of stellar systems. Topics include: meteorites, orbital dynamics, asteroids, impact craters, surfaces, atmospheres, atmospheric dynamics, interiors, magnetospheres, rings, comets, formation of planetary systems.

### SFA 185—Analysis of Development

Advanced study of basic problems in developmental biology, with major emphasis on interacting systems approached at several levels, from molecular to morphological; genetic and metabolic control of the interacting systems.

### SFA 186—Pharmacology

A study of the basic principles of pharmacology including drug solubility, absorption, and movement across body membranes. Drug distribution biotransformation and pharmaco–kinetics will be followed by a look at the quantitative basis of dosage, drug clearance by organs, dose responsive relationships, drug receptors, and the specificity of drug action. Specific drug groups to be reviewed will include (but not limited to): autonomic cholinergic agonists, anticonvulsants, antiarrhythmic, antidepressants, eicosanods, digitalis glycosides, diuretics, insulin, and oral hypoglycemic agents. Special topics will include poisons and antidotes, adverse drub reactions, and carcinogenesis and mutagenesis by xenobiotic chemicals.

### SFA 187—Chaos and Complexity

The theory and phenomenology of nonlinear dynamics and chaos in Dissapative systems. Forced and parametric oscillators. Phase space. Periodic quasiperiodic and aperiodic flows. Sensitivity to initial conditions and strange attractors. Lorenz attractor. Period doubling, intermittency and quasiperiodicity. Universality. Analysis of experimental data: Fourier transforms, Poincare sections, fractal dimension, and Lyapunov exponents.

### SFA 188—Modernism and Mass Culture

Discusses the history of painting and design in relation to emerging visual technologies, urban audiences, and consumer culture. Examines major movements and works of art, holography, design, and advertising, and investigates historical and current debates about the relationship between the transitional arts and mass culture.

### SFA 194—Plasmas

Fundamentals for plasmas on all scales: astrophysical, heliospheric, magnetospheric, and laboratory domains. Phase space distributions, Boltzmann and Vlasov–Maxwell equations, Fokker–Planck approximations, Adiabatic invariants, guiding center motion, conservation laws, viral theorem, collision–dominated plasmas, Onager relations. Approximations based on scales: MHD approximation, closure problem and break–down of differential fluid equations, discontinuities and shocks, fluctuations, linear waves.

**SFA 195—Impulse Propulsion System**

Fuel supply: primary deuterium tank; auxiliary cyro tanks; redundant cross–feed systems, anti–matter injection procedures. The main impulse engine: impulse reaction chamber; accelerator/generator; driver coil assembly, and vectored exhaust director. Impulse engine control: generic algorithms; autonomic operations; voluntary external command; field energy fratricide; translational control.

**SFA 196—Ichthyology**

A multi–disciplinary investigation of aquatic species. Topics include: general features, classification, form and function; adaptations, specializations, parallel and convergent evolution; anatomy, embryology and physiology; complement system characteristics; behavior, communication nodes, and biogeography.

**SFA 208—Dimensions in Space**

Examines how the different ways species think about space alter and change the way they conceive of space and spatial experiences; investigates how personal and cultural views of space affect ways of thinking about, constructing, and interpreting spatial experiences; looks at how institutional and religious spaces differ in their relationship to cultural and disciplinary constraints.

**SFA 211—Physical Training V**

Continuation of Physical Training IV (SFA 142) building upon the foundation laid in that course. Implementation of physical fitness regime previously developed; evaluation of program and plan modifications as necessary.

**SFA 212—Survival Training I**

Basic survival techniques in tropical and sub–tropical environments (tropical rain forest, savanna, and thorn forest/scrub); shelter, food, clothing, medical and communication considerations.

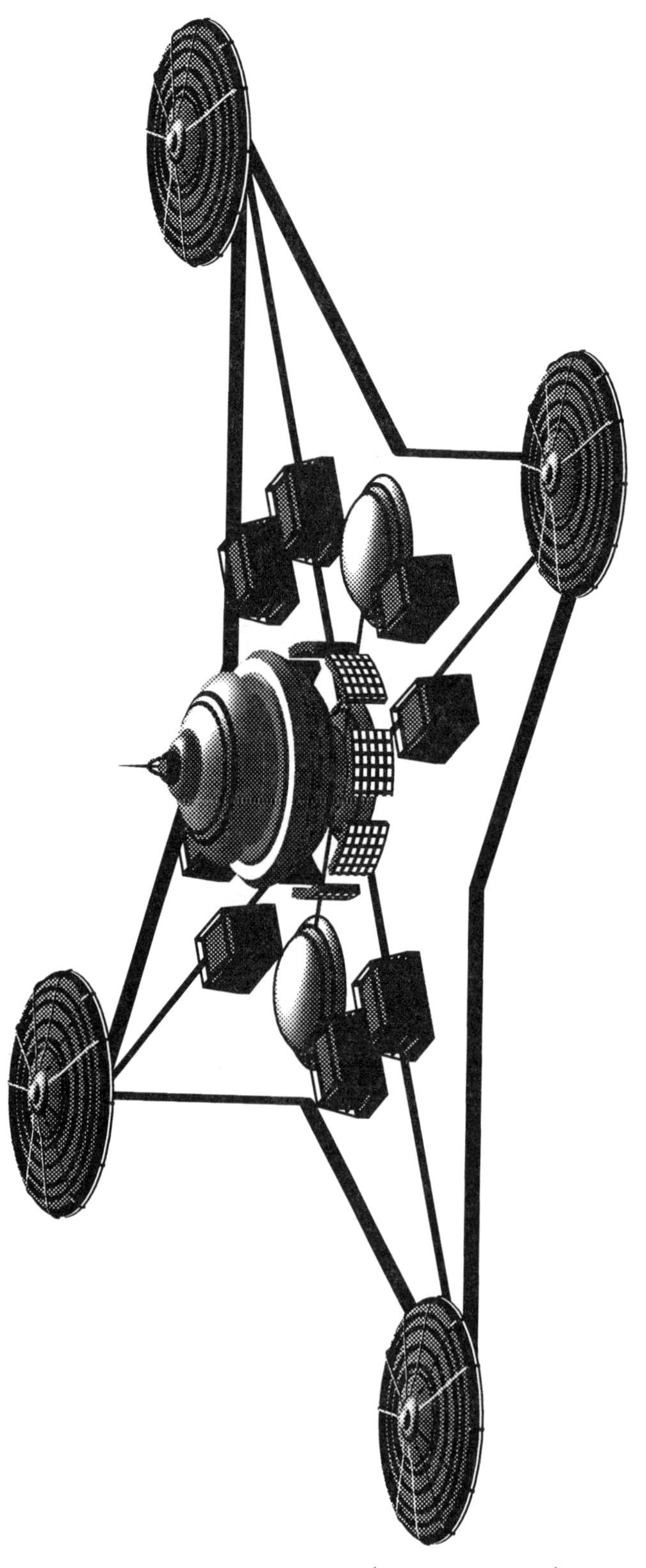

Starfleet Academy (Second Fleet)

## SFA 213—Engineering I

Overview of Engineering functions and responsibilities aboard starships: Warp engines, Impulse engines, reaction control systems, deflector shields, transporters and tactical weapons (phasers and photon torpedoes).

## SFA 214—Damage Control I

Fundamentals of compartmentalization aboard starships; material characteristics; damage control equipment and operation; internal systems preventative maintenance.

## SFA 215—Remote Sensing Packages

Development, operations, limitations and maintenance of remote sensing packages: long–range sensors, navigational sensors, and the lateral sensor array. Long– and short–range instrument probes: sensor probes, planetary probes, stellar encounter probes, reconnaissance probes, communication probes/emergency beacons, culture study probes, medium– and long–range multimission warp probes. Tricorders.

## SFA 216—Political Science I

Basic political systems; the interactions of governments and population; world governments versus independent governments; international, interplanetary, and interstellar law.

## SFA 217—Artistic Expression III

Continuation of Artistic Expression II (SFA 127) and building upon the foundation laid in that course. Integrated mediums of expression, both visual and auditory. Special projects available for the student in collaboration with faculty mentors.

## SFA 221—Physical Training VI

Continuation of Physical Training V (SFA 211) building upon the foundation laid in that course. Implementation of physical fitness regime previously developed; evaluation of program and plan modifications as necessary.

## SFA 222–Survival Training II

Continuation of Survival Training I (SFA 212) building upon the foundation laid in that course. Basic survival techniques in warm temperate environments temperate forest, grassland, shrub land and desert); shelter, food, clothing, medical and communication considerations.

**SFA 223—Engineering II**

Continuation of Engineering I (SFA 213) building upon the foundation laid in that course. Environmental systems; atmosphere and artificial gravity. Replicators and reclamation systems: food synthesizers and hardware replicators; water, sewage, solid waste, matter replicators and hazardous waste materials recycling. Auxiliary systems: turboelevators, tractor beams, utilities networks.

**SFA 224—Damage Control II**

Continuation of Damage Control I (SFA 214) building upon the foundation laid in that course. External preventative measures; EVA techniques and safety considerations; hull materials and redundant systems.

**SFA 225—Time–Series Analysis**

Statistical methods used to analyze time series. Topics: estimation of trends and seasonal components. Autocorrelation and stationarity. Models for stationary series. ARIMA models. Model specification, parameter estimation and model checking. Forecasting. Seasonal time series models. Intervention analysis and outlier detection. Fourier analysis and estimation of the spectrum. Cross–correlation and bivariate time series models. Analysis of multiple time series.

**SFA 226—Political Science II**

Continuation of Political Science I (SFA 216) building upon the foundation laid in that course. The United Federation of Planets' purpose, authority and organization; UFP relationships with non–aligned worlds and multi–planet political entities; current treaties and relationships with hostile and non–hostile governmental organizations.

**SFA 227—Artistic Expression IV**

Continuation of Artistic Expression III (SFA 217) and building upon the foundation laid in that course. Special projects at the student's discretion in collaboration with faculty/civilian mentors.

### SFA 231—Physical Training VII

Continuation of Physical Training VI (SFA 221) building upon the foundation laid in that course. Implementation of physical fitness regime previously developed; evaluation of program and plan modifications as necessary.

### SFA 232—Survival Training III

Continuation of Survival Training II (SFA 222) building upon the foundation laid in that course. Basic survival techniques in cold–temperate and Arctic–alpine environments (taiga and tundra); shelter, food, clothing, medical and communication considerations.

### SFA 233—Diophantine Geometry

Diophantine equations over finite fields, Weil zeta function, applications to linear codes. Diophantine equations over number fields, heights, introduction to Arakelov geometry. Zeta functions and motives, values at integral points, K–theory, polylogarithms. Modular forms.

### SFA 234—Lie Groups

Symplectic geometry, Hamiltonian mechanics, and the Poisson structure. Hamilton–Jacobi theory, Lagrangian systems, and foundations of mathematical physics. Lagrangian submanifolds, caustics, and the Maslov class. Completely integrable systems and conservation laws. Coadjoint orbits and the moment map. Geometric quantization, Borel–Weil–Bott, Stone–von Neuman, and the metaplectic representation.

### SFA 235—Starfleet Vessels Characteristics

Classification, types and characteristics of Starfleet vessels including auxiliary, support and capital ships; advantages and disadvantages of each; primary, secondary, and tertiary roles; use of appropriate mission–selection criteria.

### SFA 236—Logistics in Starfleet

An overview of the role of logistics in Starfleet operations. The four basic logistical components: supply, transportation, facilities, and personnel services. Types of supply: initial issue, replacement and resupply. Forms of transportation: transport ships, tugs, cargo carriers (freighters and other commercial carriers), the impact of replication. Facility operations: factories, arsenals, laboratories, warehouses, hospitals and barracks. Personnel services: hospitalization and evacuation, military justice and discipline, custody of prisoners of war, and civil affairs, personnel administration, training, and nontactical construction.

### SFA 237—Starbase Operations

The Starbase as an integral part of Starfleet operations and strategy; the different types of starbases; intricacies in effective operation and organization of Starbases in various roles such as ship repair facilities, forward bases, economic centers, transfer points, and recreation. The K–7, REGULA–1 Type, and the Type 79 Starbase; future designs.

### SFA 241—Fast Cruise

Utilizing the heavy cruiser mock–up USS NEVERSAIL (NCC–0000), the student will live aboard a simulated starship, standing watches, performing maintenance and accomplishing day–to–day duties in every area of the ship on a rotating basis. Random emergency situations will be interjected to familiarize students with operational, tactical, and strategic considerations.

### SFA 242—Survival Experience IV

Continuation of Survival Training III (SFA 232) building upon the foundation laid in that course. Survival simulation. Students will be paired and placed on a randomly selected planet containing one of the major environments with minimal supplies for a period of 30 days to demonstrate the ability to survive utilizing the skills and knowledge gained from completion of SFA 212,222, and 232.

### SFA 249—Topics in Nonlinear Dynamics of Dissapative Systems

A detailed introduction to selected advanced topics in the nonlinear dynamics of high–dimensional, spatially extended Dissapative systems. Includes discussions of basic theory and phenomenology in addition to various numerical methods useful for computational studies. Areas of study include fluid dynamics, fracture, phase transitions, percolation, and growth. Analysis of models of dynamical systems, including flow through porous media. Cellular automata.

### SFA 260—Relativistic Quantum Field Theory

Relativistic quantum field theory, stressing the formulation of gauge field theory and its application to fundamental physical problems. Classical field theory, canonical quantization, the Dirac field. Interacting field and perturbation theory, Feynman graphs.

Symmetries. Calculations in quantum electrodynamics. Functional integral formulation of gauge theories. Divergences, regularization, and renormalization. Higher–order processes in electro-dynamics. Fundamental constituents of matter; the standard models of electro, weak, and strong interaction. Non–abelian gauge theories, spontaneous symmetry breakdown, the Goldstone and Higgs mechanisms. The Weinberg–Salam theory. Renormalization group.

**SFA 269—Ornithology**

A multi–disciplinary investigation of airborne species. Topics include: general features, classification, form and function; adaptations, specializations, parallel and convergent evolution; anatomy, embryology and physiology; complement system characteristics; behavior, communication nodes, and biogeography.

**SFA 272—Fundamentals of Ecology**

The science of ecology; principles of interrelationships between organisms and their environment. Development of basic concepts of energy flow and biogeochemical cycles in ecosystems; productivity; trophic dynamics; community structure and stability; competition and predation; evolution and natural selection; population growth; and physiological ecology.

**SFA 276—Clinical Laboratory Methods**

Review of laboratory rules and quality control. Clinical laboratory safety and procedures will precede the presentation of specimen collection and preparation. An overview of hemoglobin investigation, blood group systems, and blood banking is followed by lab work in special test procedures. Immunohematology, clinical chemistry, microbiology, serology, and immunology work will also be reviewed.

**SFA 285—Care Procedures**

Both classroom and lab work related to the basics of individual patient care. Vital signs and physical examinations, safety, hygiene, nutrition, elimination, transfer, discharge, and terminal care; introduction to mobility including body mechanics and transfer techniques, body position, mobility and special beds. Infection control, diagnostic testing, physical treatments, intravenous therapy, drug administration and recent development in medical equipment will be followed by specific types of care including: cardiovascular, respiratory, gastrointestinal, renal and urologic, neurologic, orthopedic, skin, ear, nose and throat, obstetric and gynecologic, neonatal and pediatric care.

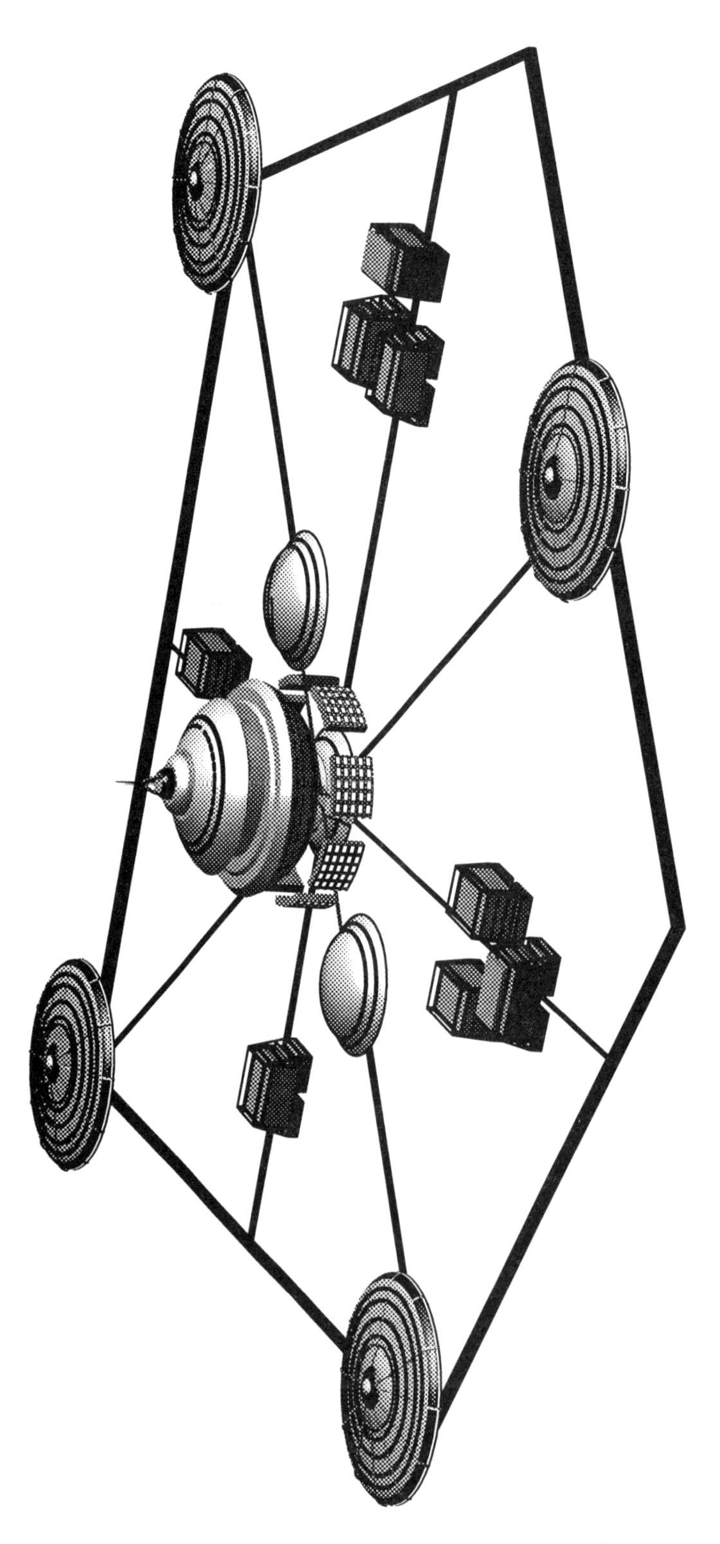

Starfleet Academy (Third Fleet)

### SFA 292—Mammalogy

A multi–disciplinary investigation of mammaloids. Topics include: general features, classification, form and function; adaptations, specializations, parallel and convergent evolution; anatomy, embryology and physiology; complement system characteristics; behavior, communications nodes, and biogeography.

### SFA 296—Utilities Networks

Power; Optical Data Network; atmospheric ducting; water conduits; linear induction utility conduits; transporter beam waveguides; replicator and food service systems; structural integrity field power conduits; inertial dampening field conduits; synthetic gravity field bleed; cryogenic fluid transfer, deuterium fuel transfers; reserve and protected utilities distribution; Jefferies Tubes; auxiliary fusion generators.

### SFA 299—Landsurface–Atmosphere Interaction

Examination of the processes that govern the exchange of mass, heat, and momentum between the atmosphere and soil, vegetation, and open–water surfaces. Techniques for the estimation of moisture and energy balance at the surface. Evapotranspiration and hydrothermal flux in the soil column. Diagnostics of the global cycles of moisture and heat; interactions and feedbacks in the coupled system. Use of remote sensing techniques and observational tools in sampling surface and atmospheric conditions. Numerical and conceptual models for the simulation of heat and moisture exchange in the planet–atmosphere–ocean system.

### SFA 302—Anthropology

What kinds of wisdom do other ways of life offer our own? How do other perspectives challenge our assumptions about life? These questions are addressed through the four fields of anthropology: biological, cultural, linguistic anthropology and archaeology. Examination of family and kinship, religion, economics, politics, survival of indigenous groups, and Federation influences from an anthropological perspective to gain appreciation for cultural and ethnic diversity.

### SFA 303—Biological Chemistry

Description of the organization and functioning of living organisms in terms of molecular structures and processes. Chemical and physical properties of cell and tissue constitutes including carbohydrates, lipids, nucleic acids, and proteins. Origin of catalysis in biological systems. Metabolic synthesis and degradation of amino acids, simple carbohydrates, fats, and origins and fates of macro–molecules as well as chemical bases of regulation and integration of metabolic phenomena.

**SFA 304—Structural Mechanics**

Applies solid mechanics to analysis of high–technology structures. Structural design considerations. Three–dimensional elasticity theory; stress, anisotropic materials, heating effects. Two–dimensional plane stress and plane strain problems. Torsion theory for arbitrary sections. Bending, shear, and torsion of unsymmetric section and thin–wall beams. Buckling of columns and stability phenomena. Structural dynamics including influence coefficients, modeling, vibration modes, normal equations of motion, dynamic response to sinusoidal and arbitrary forces.

**SFA 305—Planetary Systems**

Introduction to the study of planetary systems. An overview of planetary systems, planetary orbits, rings, planetary formation, meteorites, asteroids, comets, planetary surfaces and cratering, planetary interiors, planetary atmospheres and lifeforms.

**SFA 311—Physical Training VIII**

Continuation of Physical Training VII (SFA 231) building upon the foundation laid in the course. Implementation of physical fitness regime previously developed; evaluation of program and plan modifications as necessary.

**SFA 312—Commercial Vessels**

Design and operating characteristics; identification and capabilities of civilian commercial vessels including passenger ships, freighters, colony transports, yachts, and mobile repair facilities. Established shipping lanes and current shipping schedules. Warning buoys, communications relay stations and queue theory. The commercial carrier as a Starfleet auxiliary vessel.

**SFA 313—Science I**

Investigation of life sciences, social sciences and medicine; sensor interpretation in these specialized fields. Special projects available for the student in collaboration with a faculty mentor.

## SFA 314—Basic Security Operations

Design, deployment, and duties of security forces aboard ships, on starbases, and at planetary facilities. The role of security in patrol, protection, and defense modes. Integration of Starfleet Marine forces with ship and/or station personnel. Identification of friend or foe, an investigation of the escalation concept of security responses, and threat analysis. The role of non–security forces and civilians in the defense of personnel and facilities. Extensive use of holodeck scenarios.

## SFA 315—Bridge Systems

Modular Bridge systems: Integrated and isolated operation of all bridge stations of a standard bridge module; basic techniques of various stations such as helm, navigation, communications, operations, weapons, engineering and science. Specialized modules, their design, use, and replacement.

## SFA 316—Starfleet History

Initial concepts behind the inclusion of Starfleet in the Articles of Federation; the beginnings; significant philosophical changes; pivotal actions and their impact on Starfleet and the UFP; important individual contributions; current concepts; the future of Starfleet.

## SFA 320—Current Topics in Life Sciences

Guest lecturers present on varied topics of current interest in the field of Life Sciences. Interactive discussions of presentations/lectures/exhibits with panels of experts and/or individuals. Lectures and topics subject to change based on availability, emergent findings, and immediacy of subjects.

## SFA 321—Physical Training IX

Continuation of Physical Training VIII (SFA 311) building upon the foundation laid in that course. Implementation of physical fitness regime previously developed; evaluation of program and plan modifications as necessary.

## SFA 322—Programming Models

Covers practical applications of mathematical programming modeling techniques, including linear programming, integer programming, quadratic programming, linear programming with uncertainty, and multiple objective programming.

### SFA 323—Science II

Continuation of Science I (SFA 313) building upon the foundation laid in that course. Investigation into physical and space sciences; the interrelationship between social sciences, physical sciences, space sciences and life sciences; sensor interpretation. Special projects available for the student in collaboration with a faculty mentor.

### SFA 324—Individual Ship Tactics

Concepts of the single starship in hostile situations; study of classic single–ship confrontations: The Corbomite Escape, Kirk Defense Pivot; April Maneuver, Sulu maneuver, Fire–Blossom Ploy and others; non–hostile responses to adversarial situations.

### SFA 325—Strategy and Tactics I

Historical use of military and para–military organizations; organization of land, air, and sea units; famous confrontations, their strategies and conceptual tactics; intended and unintended consequences; diplomacy versus force.

### SFA 326—Decision Analysis

Basic theory of decision making under conditions of uncertainty. Topics: decision trees, quantification of judgments and preferences, the value of information, Gayes theorem, the structuring of complex decisions, and multi–attributed utility theory.

### SFA 329—Biology

Exploration into areas of current research in cell biology, immunology, neurobiology, developmental biology, and evolution. Application of the fundamental principles toward an understanding of cells, humanoid genetics and diseases, infectious agents, the immune system and evolution. Application of the fundamental principles toward an understanding of microorganisms as geochemical agents responsible for the evolution and renewal of the biosphere.

### SFA 331—Physical Training X

Continuation of Physical Training IV (SFA 321) building upon the foundation laid in that course. Implementation of physical fitness regime previously developed; evaluation of program and plan modifications as necessary.

### SFA 332—Strategy and Tactics II

Continuation of Strategy and Tactics I (SFA 325) building upon the foundation laid in that course. The starship as a military unit in both individual and combined operations; effective utilization of three–dimensional capabilities.

### SFA 333—Tactical Weapons

Familiarization with and the use of personal weapons including the phaser, phaser rifle, assault rifle and grenade launcher; familiarization with and the use of ship's phasers and photon torpedoes.

### SFA 334—Advanced Security Operations

Continuation of Basic Security Operations (SFA 314) and building upon the foundation laid in that course. Hostage situations, terrorists acts, illegal or banned weapons response, heavy weapons, overcoming entrenched adversaries, undercover operations, Starfleet Intelligence.

### SFA 335—Life Support Systems

Operation, maintenance, and repair of shipboard life–support systems including artificial gravity, environmental controls, and closed–system recovery operations. Overview of hydroponics.

### SFA 336—Emergency Procedures

A two–part class investigating individual and tactical responses to life–threatening situations. Part 1 deals with shipboard emergencies: intruder alert, life support failure (gravity, atmosphere, inertia dampening system), abandon ship, lifeboats (characteristics, operations and controls) shipboard area evacuation, loss of hull integrity, and saucer separation. Part 2 investigates localized and planetary–scale scenarios: medical emergencies (disease, accident/incident, mass casualties), mass evacuations (methods, security, constraints). Historical and theoretical scenarios investigated through extensive use of holodecks.

### SFA 341—Fast Cruise

Utilizing the heavy cruiser mock–up USS NEVERSAIL (NCC–0000), the student will live aboard a simulated starship, standing watches, performing maintenance and accomplishing day–to–day duties in every area of the ship on a rotating basis. Random emergency situations will be interjected to familiarize students with operational, tactical, and strategic considerations.

### SFA 342—Current Topics

Investigation into current topics of interest to future Starfleet officers; subjects may include political, economic, social, legal, scientific, tactical or strategic situations of immediate concern. Presented during Fast Cruise (SFA—341).

### SFA 352—High–Energy Astrophysics

Observation and theory of high–energy phenomena and processes in astrophysics. Relative processes, including Bremsstrahlung radiation, synchrotron radiation, Compton scattering, coherent emission. Relativistic shock waves and other relativistic phenomena. Spherical and disk accretion theory. Neutron stars; pulsars; black holes. Application to galactic X–ray sources, quasars, and active galactic nuclei.

### SFA 363—Selected Topics in Physical Sciences

Guest lecturers present on varies topics of current interest in the field of Physical Sciences. Interactive discussions of presentations/lectures/exhibits with panels of experts and/or individuals. Lectures and topics subject to change based on availability, emergent findings, and immediacy of subjects.

### SFA 366—Anatomy I

Study of humanoid and non–humanoid body structures including scalp, cranium, meninges and brain; regions about the mouth; regions within the buccal cavity; tonsillar and pharynx region; anterior, lateral, and thoracocervical regions of the neck. The thorax in general to include thoracic walls and the thoracic cavity and its contents will be followed by an examination of the abdominal wall and the abdominal cavity and contents.

### SFA 367—Anatomy II

Continuation of Anatomy I (SFA 366) building upon the foundation laid in that course. Particular attention given to the pelvis, perineum, the upper extremities and the lower extremities. Students are to perform basic dissection, isolation, and removal of body structures on humanoids and non–humanoids using accepted laboratory procedures and to report progress in lab analysis on a weekly basis.

## SFA 370—Stellar Structure and Evolution

Observable stellar characteristics; overview of observational information. Principles underlying calculations of stellar structure. Physical processes in stellar interiors; properties of matter and radiation; radiative, conductive, and convective heat transport; nuclear energy generation; nucleosynthesis; neutrino emission. Protostars; the main sequence, and the solar neutrino flux; advanced evolutionary states; variable stars; planetary nebulae, supernovae, white dwarfs, and neutrons stars; close binary systems; chemical elements.

## SFA 372—Adolescent Health Care

An examination of the principles of adolescent medicine including a historical perspective on the history of adolescence and evolution of adolescent behavior. Growth and development, evaluation of the patient, treatment issues, and the psychomedical approach are all covered in some depth. Specific adolescent medical disorders will be followed by a closer look at psychosocial issues and the adolescent with special attention given to family relationships, cultural and social influences, sexuality issues, and problem behaviors. Orthopedics and sports medicine will also be examined.

## SFA 377—Geriatric Medicine

An overview of gerontology and the general principles of aging. Geriatric medicine will look at problems specific to the aging population including falls, dementia and delirium, neuropathology of old age, cardiac arrhythmias, valvular heart disease, chronic cardiac failure and management of the ischemic heart. Care of the elderly will be discussed with special attention being given to issues concerning promotion of health and prevention, rehabilitation, psychogeriatric services, and care of the dying.

## SFA 381—Projects in Knowledge Representations

Focus on building practical domain representations for intelligent systems and introducing students to a variety of representation toolkits. Students gain sophistication in the design and critique of representation systems as well as practical skills in application specification and interface design.

## SFA 384—Introduction to Psychology

A survey of humanoid and non–humanoid mental life and behavior. Explores sensation, perception, learning, memory, thinking, feeling, emotion, motivation, personality. Uses psychological, social and biological data. Considers cultural, political, and literary impact of psychology.

**SFA 393—Warp Propulsion I**

Theory and application: Zefram Cochrane; continuum distortion propulsion, non–Newtonian methodology; asymmetrical peristaltic field manipulation; General, Special and Transformational Relativity. Warp power measurement: Cochrane's; apparent versus actual values; quantum drag forces; motive power oscillation inefficiencies; peak transitional thresholds. Theoretical limits. Intro to warp propulsion systems.

**SFA 394—Warp Propulsion II**

Continuation of Warp Propulsion I (SFA 393) and building upon the foundation laid in that course. Matter/antimatter Reaction Assembly: reactant injectors; magnetic constriction segments; matter/antimatter reaction chamber; power transfer conduits. Warp field nacelles; warp field coils; plasma injection system; emergency separation system; maintenance docking port. Antimatter storage and transfer: fuel supply. Bussard Ramscoop. On–board antimatter generation.

**SFA 397—Interstellar Shipping**

Explores internal operating, financial, and marketing issues as well as external market and technological factors that define the interstellar shipping environment. Includes effect of energy prices and changing trade patterns on demand for shipping; evaluation of shipping capacity requirements in terms of capital needs; new ship and terminal technologies; and the effect of changing interstellar relationships.

**SFA 400—Auxiliary Systems**

External connect hardpoints; turboelevators; corridor access; umbilical resupply connect points. Tractor beam: emitters; graviton polarity; subspace field amplifiers. Autodestruct systems. Waste management: water and sewage recycling; solid waste recycling; matter replication recycling; hazardous waste recycling.

**SFA 401—Asteroids and Small Bodies**

Introduction to the study of asteroids and the techniques used to explore them. Topics include asteroid orbital properties, surface structure, physical properties, and classifications, as well as their origin, thermal and collisional evolution, and interrelationships with meteorites and comets. The probabilities and consequences of planetary collisions.

**SFA 406—Biogeography**

Major concepts and theories and historical biogeography including a discussion of the principles of population ecology and recent developments in numerical biogeography. Incorporates a broad outline of the regional patterns of planet and animal development.

**SFA 410—Physical Methods in Inorganic Chemistry**

Physical methods and their application to inorganic chemical compounds. Includes diffraction methods; electronic photoelectron spectroscopy; vibrational and rotational spectroscopy; magnetic measurements; including magnetic and electron spin resonance; Mossbauer spectroscopy; mass spectrometry; electrochemical measurements. Case histories with the complementary use of selections of the various methods described.

**SFA 411—Physical Training XI**

Continuation of Physical Training X (SFA 331) building upon the foundation laid in that course. Implementation of physical fitness regime previously developed; evaluation of program and plan modifications as necessary.

**SFA 412—War and War Prevention**

Examines the causes of war with a focus on practical measures to prevent and control war. Topics: causes and consequences of misperception; arms races and war; accidental war; UFP policy as a cause of war and peace; and the likelihood and possible nature of another interstellar war.

**SFA 413—Shuttlecraft Operations I**

Operations systems and maintenance; theoretical applications of craft in landing operations; utilization of shuttlecraft in offensive and defense scenarios; controls, limitations, and design considerations.

**SFA 414—Intercultural Relations I**

The cultures of Federation member worlds; acceptance of non–norms; integration of societies; religious considerations.

Starfleet Academy (Fourth Fleet)

### SFA 415—Federation Law I

Basic law systems; rights, responsibilities and consequences; the Court System; case law and appropriate venues; the appeal process.

### SFA 416—Diplomacy I

Relationships within the United Federation of Planets; diplomatic considerations and the officer's role in maintaining relationships across United Federation of Planets categories.

### SFA 420—Hexapodology

A multi–disciplinary investigation of insectoids. Topics include: general features, classification, form and function; adaptations, specializations, parallel and convergent evolution; anatomy, embryology and physiology; complement system characteristics; behavior, communication nodes and biogeography.

### SFA 421—Physical Training XII

Continuation of Physical Training XI (SFA 411) building upon the foundation laid in that course. Implementation of physical fitness regime previously developed; evaluation of program and plan modifications as necessary.

### SFA 422—Technical Communication

Students intensively review the elements of sentence and paragraph structure; special problems in organizing and condensing technical information; and strategies for writing technical descriptions, definitions, classifications, and analyses. Writing to different audiences and preparing brief proposals, lab reports, graphics.

### SFA 423—Shuttlecraft Operations II

The shuttlecraft in flight; navigation, helm, engineering aspects; flight operations and piloting. Student will graduate with a Novice Pilot Classification License.

### SFA 424—Intercultural Relations II

Continuation of Intercultural Relations I (SFA 414) building upon the foundation laid in that course. Non–Federation worlds; social taboos; sexual relationships; humanoid and non–humanoid confrontations, and conflict resolution.

**SFA 425—Federal Law II**

Continuation of Federal Law I (SFA 415) building upon the foundation laid in that course. Starfleet discipline procedures and their relationship with traditional military justice and Federation law; the judicial systems' hierarchy; precedence and case studies of precedence.

**SFA 426—Diplomacy II**

Continuation of Diplomacy I (SFA 416) building upon the foundations laid in that course. Relationships with political entities external to the United Federation of Planets. Treaty development; trade agreements; legal ramifications of diplomatic actions; cross–cultural considerations. The role of the starship commander.

**SFA 431—Training Cruise**

Students will go aboard the Academy's Training Vessel and fulfill duty watches aboard a starship during routine operations in space for acclimation. Duration: 100 days. For more detail, see the discussion on Training Cruise elsewhere in this Handbook.

**SFA 436—Comparative Value Systems**

Comparative treatment of values, views, belief systems of selected societies; basic premises and tenets revealed in a society's interpretation of its experiences; examination of relation between values, world views.

**SFA 437—Systematic Climatology**

An analysis of factors affecting climatic variations and types, particularly solar and planetary radiation, temperature conditions, atmospheric pressure and wind patterns, and moisture and precipitation and characteristics.

**SFA 441—Physical Training XIII**

Continuation of Physical Training XII (SFA 421) building upon the foundation laid in that course. Implementation of physical fitness regime previously developed; evaluation of program and plan modifications as necessary.

### SFA 442—Ethics

Systematic study of central theories in ethics, including egoism, act and rule utilitarianism, intuitionism, emotivism, rights theories, and contractualism. Discussion and readings also focus on problems associated with moral conflicts, justice, the relationship between rightness and goodness, objective vs. subjective moral judgments, moral truth and relativism.

### SFA 444—Diplomacy III

Continuation of Diplomacy II (SFA 426) building upon the foundation laid in that course. Force as a last resort; unintended consequences; negotiation; mechanics of acceptance; use of subterfuge and misdirection; multi–party agreements.

### SFA 445—Logic

The aims and techniques of formal logic. The logic of truth functions and quantifies. The concepts of validity and truth and their relation to formal deduction. Application of logic and the place of logic. The completeness of predicate logic, recursive functions, the incompleteness of arithmetic, the uprovability of consistency, the indefinability of truth, Skolem–Lowenheim theorems, non–standard models.

### SFA 446—Command and Control

The concepts, theory, operation and utilization of on–scene command and control of various operating categories such as the individual, groups, starships operating independently and larger combined units.

### SFA 450—Nutrition

The fundamentals of nutritional science starting with a basic review of digestion, absorption and metabolism. Discussion of dietary guides, food composition, proteins and amino acids, carbohydrates, lipids, energy metabolism and mineral elements will be followed with current information on fluid balance, fat–soluble vitamins, water–soluble vitamins and the Vitamin B Complex. Factors influencing food intake and cultural food patterns will be investigated.

### SFA 451—Particle Physics

Thermal equilibrium states in quantum field theories. Phase transitions and the fate of the false vacuum. Homotropy theory and topological defects; monopoles, strings, and domain walls. The standard cosmological model. The inflationary universe. Quantum field theory in de Sitter space. Quantum origin of density fluctuations in inflationary models.

### SFA 458—Physical Examinations

The initial patient interview and history process along with examination techniques and equipment will begin this course. Examination of specific body area include the exo–derm or exo–skeleton, lymphatic system, heart and blood vessels, abdomen, genitalia, and neurologic systems. Finally, the general guidelines of examination and examination sequence will be examined. The assessment of emergency situations with specific attention to the ABCs and injury assessment will conclude the course.

### SFA 463—Economics of Uncertainty

Static choice theory: utility, expected utility, and non–expected utility theory; risk and risk aversion. Dynamic choice theory: optimal search, price search, "classic" models of non–price search, price search equilibrium; optimal auctions, revenue equivalence, mechanism design, auctions with risk aversion or correlated values; Bayesian learning, sampling with learning, experimentation, the two–armed bandit; dynamic decision analysis, informational externalities, probabilistic reasoning.

### SFA 474—Continuum Mechanics

Practical applications of the continuum concept for deformation of solids and fluids, emphasizing force balance. Stress tensor, infinitesimal and finite strain, and rotation tensors developed. Constitutive relations applicable to geological materials, including elastic, viscous, brittle, and plastic deformation. Solutions to classical problems in geodynamics, physical oceanography, and atmospheric sciences.

### SFA 476—Astrophysics

Size and time scales in astrophysics. Stellar structure equations and survey of stellar evolution. Degenerate stars and interacting binary stars. Radiative transfer, line formation, spectroscopy of interstellar medium. The equilibrium of stellar systems and the distribution of stars in the Milky Way Galaxy. Introduction to cosmology.

### SFA 480—Defects in Crystals

Unified treatment of point, line, and planar defects in crystals. Point defects include vacancies, self–interstitials, and solute atoms. Line defects include dislocations. planar defects include stacking faults, small– and large–angle grain boundaries, and interphase boundaries. Discusses geometrical structure and physical properties such as stress fields, energies, and mobilities. Treats interactions between defects including point defect clustering, point defect–dislocation pinning, dislocation climb, and grain boundaries as point defect sources/sinks.

### SFA 497—Selected Topics in Engineering

Guest lecturers present on varies topics of current interest in the field of Engineering. Interactive discussions of presentations/lectures/exhibits with panels of experts and/or individuals. Lectures and topics subject to change based on availability, emergent findings, and immediacy of subjects.

USS BENNINGTON (NCC-1978)

# GENERAL ORDERS

General Orders are the basic guiding principles by which Starfleet personnel are governed. Every member is required to follow both the letter and the intent of each. Failure to do so can result in serious consequences.

Six General Orders were established when the Federation was originally founded. Over time, another 19 were added. The increasing number of General Orders became unwieldy and, in some cases, excessively restrictive. A Blue Ribbon Panel of the Military Staff Committee was established to rewrite and consolidate these 25 General Orders into a more concise set of directives.

The following 10 General Orders were adopted in 2301. Any further modifications require approval by the Federation Council.

## GENERAL ORDER #1

Starfleet personnel may not interfere with the cultural, social, or historical development of a sentient race or species not a member of the United Federation of Planets. Such interference includes introducing superior knowledge or technology to the sentient race or species, informing the sentient race or species that worlds or lifeforms other than their own exist outside the confines of their own space, or any other action which would alter the normal evolution of a sentient race or species. This General Order supersedes all other considerations, including the duty of a starship commander to safeguard ship and crew.

## GENERAL ORDER #2

No Starfleet personnel may use unnecessary force against any member of a sentient race or species.

## GENERAL ORDER #3

Starfleet personnel shall observe any and all statutes, laws, ordinances, rules of governance, and social customs in effect within the jurisdiction of an independent planetary system or government, or a member planet of the United Federation of Planets. Any violation will be dealt with in accordance with the local laws and customs. The senior Starfleet representative is required to extradite any person over which jurisdiction is held upon the application of an authorized civilian official.

## GENERAL ORDER #4

Any request for emergency assistance from a member planet of the United Federation of Planets or a Federation citizen takes precedence over any scheduled or contemplated action by Starfleet personnel. Starfleet personnel will respond to any such request immediately.

## GENERAL ORDER #5

Starship commanders are to consider their crew's lives as sacred and will place the crew's lives and well–being above the ship's safety.

## GENERAL ORDER #6

Starfleet personnel will employ any means necessary to prevent the possession, transportation, sale, or exchange of sentient beings held against their wishes within the boundaries of Federation space.

## GENERAL ORDER #7

No Starfleet vessel shall approach within 10 Astronomical Units of the Planet Talos IV under any circumstances. Any violation of this General Order shall be punishable by death.

## GENERAL ORDER #8

When verifiable proof is presented to the commander of any Starfleet unit that a Federation representative is violating or has violated General Order #1, that officer will relieve the representative of all duties, assume the full powers vested in the representative, and confine the representative pending an investigation by an appropriate governmental entity.

## GENERAL ORDER #9

No Starfleet personnel will violate Neutral Zone boundaries or the territorial integrity of independent planetary systems or governments unless so ordered by competent authority.

# GENERAL ORDER #10

Any individual who is taken into custody by Starfleet personnel shall be accorded proper and appropriate treatment consistent with that individual's rank or station so long as that treatment does not compromise the security of the United Federation of Planets, Starfleet, or an individual Starfleet unit.

Front Entrance, Main Administration Building

Hull STARGAZER, Starfleet Academy (Fourth Fleet)

# LEXICON

**Abaft**: Behind or farther aft; astern or toward the stern.

**Abandon Ship**: An order to all personnel to leave a stricken ship according to a pre-established plan of action, including lifeboats and auxiliary craft.

**Abeam**: At right angles to the centerline of and outside a ship.

**Aboard**: On or in a ship.

**Adrift**: Loose from mooring without power; out of place; out of control or lost.

**Aft**: In, near, or toward the stern of a ship.

**After**: That which is farthest aft.

**Ahead**: Forward of the bow of a ship.

**Alongside**: By the side of a ship.

**Amidships**: Indefinite area midway between bow and stern; in the middle portion of the ship, along the line of the keel.

**Armament**: Ship's weapons.

**Ashore**: On a planetary surface or starbase; not on the ship.

**Astern**: Toward the stern; an object or vessel that is abaft another vessel or object; directly behind a ship—Bearing 180 Mark 0.

**Athwart**: Across; at right angles to.

**Authorized Grade**: The minimum level (either officer or enlisted) of expertise which is appropriate for that specific position listed in the SMD.

**Auxiliary**: Extra or secondary.

**Auxiliary Bridge**: Located deep within the primary hull, also known as the Secondary Bridge. It replicates each station on the Main Bridge, although not necessarily the physical layout. Its purpose is to provide the ship with command, control, and communication functions should the Main Bridge become damaged or uninhabitable for whatever reason. It is manned during Red Alerts and when so ordered by the Commanding Officer or Officer-of-the-Deck by qualified personnel as indicated in the SMD.

**Aye Aye**: Reply to a command meaning "I understand and will comply."

**Azimuth**: See bearing.

**Back**: To go backwards.

**Bank**: Pair (or larger group) of similar weapons, fired as a unit.

**Beam**: Width; breadth; greatest athwartships width of a vessel; the extreme breadth of a ship.

**Bearing**: The direction of an object from an observer; first measured in degrees clockwise from dead ahead along the ship's X—Y plane, second measured in degrees upward or downward from said X—Y plane.

**Belay**: To countermand or cancel a previous order or action.

**Below**: Downward from a position.

**Berth**: Mooring space assigned to a ship.

**Billet**: Place or duty to which one is assigned.

**Billet Sequence Code** (BSC): An unique number assigned to each position listed in the SMD. Every individual assigned to a Starfleet command (starship or starbase) has a BSC which not only identifies that person's position but is also used by the Main Library Computer for security access to classified information.

**Board**: The act of going aboard a ship; a group of persons meeting for a specific purpose.

**Bow**: The forward end of a vessel.

**Break Out**: To unstow or prepare for use.

**Bridge**: Area from which a ship is controlled.

**Brig**: Prison on a ship or Starbase.

**Broad**: Wide.

**Broadside To**: At right angles to the fore-and-aft line of a ship.

**BSC**: See Billet Sequence Code.

**Bulkhead**: A vertical partition (wall) separating two compartments (rooms).

**Buoy**: A free-floating object in space designed for a specific task, such as communications, navigation, etc.

**Burdened Vessel**: That vessel which does not have the right of way.

*c*: A representation of the speed of light in a vacuum; $2.9979 \times 10^8$ meters per second.

**Cabin**: Living quarters aboard a ship.

**Captain's Gig**: A small, easily stowed, five-passenger shuttle carried aboard larger starships which is used to ferry personnel from ship to ship or from ship to station, primarily as a diplomatic gesture.

**Carry Away**: To break loose or tear loose.

**Cathedral Unit**: A test crew of personnel from the Starfleet Corps of Engineers and Starfleet Tactical which takes prototypes out on their shakedown cruise and evaluates the performance of all systems. Its name is taken from the secluded and cordoned-off sector reserved for this purpose.

**Centerline**: Imaginary line running from the ship's bow to its stern.

**Chief Engineer**: The senior member of the Engineering Department. This individual is responsible for the operation, maintenance, and repair of propulsion, weapons, and other operational systems aboard the ship or starbase.

**Chief of Security**: The senior member of the Security Department. This individual is responsible for protecting crew members on board the ship from potential injury or death, crewmembers off the ship on authorized landing parties, and to protect vital and sensitive areas of the ship or starbase as designated by the Commanding Officer.

**Chief Medical Officer**: The senior member of the Medical Department. This individual is responsible for the health and welfare of every member of the crew, maintenance of all medical records, and other duties as assigned by the Commanding Officer.

**Chain of Command**: Succession of officers through which command is exercised from superior to subordinate. Aboard most Starfleet ships and starbases, the chain of command is: Commanding Officer, First Officer (Executive Officer), Operations Officer, Chief Science Officer, Chief Engineer, Chief Security Officer, Logistics Officer, Chief Medical Officer.

**Chart**: Usually holographic, a map of a volume of space showing stellar positions, traffic lanes, buoys, and navigational hazards.

**Close Aboard**: Near a ship.

**Cold Iron**: A condition of a vessel when it is not generating its own power; required power is provided by a Starbase or another vessel.

**Colors**: United Federation of Planets' flag; command to raise or lower same.

**Commanding Officer**: The senior Starfleet officer aboard any commissioned vessel or starbase. A commanding officer has numerous responsibilities for both the command and the area of the Federation in which the command is operating. Among these are: military commander of any space sector in which the ship is located (including assembling ships in a fleet, mounting or reacting to an attack, and declaring the specific section to be in a state of combat); military governor of any colonies, outposts, or expeditions in the sector (final arbiter of the disbursement of materials, persons, or facilities to these outposts; authorized to settle any disputes over claims or territorial rights); supervisor of interstellar commerce, trade, or shipping in the section; aiding or restricting such trade according to the current conditions or requirements of the Federation; the official representative of the Federation to any aligned or unaligned worlds or peoples in the section (having the power to open negotiations, arrange for trade and cultural exchange, and make temporary treaties of peace or partnership); responsible for the protection and stewardship of underdeveloped worlds and peoples according to the Prime Directive; serves as chief legal official of the Federation; possesses complete authority over all personnel assigned to his or her ship.

**Commission**: To activate a ship; a written order giving an officer his/her rank and authority.

**Communicator**: Personal transceiver.

**Companionway**: Deck opening giving access to a ladder.

**Compartment**: Interior space of a ship (room).

**Conn**: To direct a helmsman as to movement of helm; the act of controlling a ship.

**Convoy**: A number of merchant ships sailing under the escort of warships; the act of escorting such ships.

**Course**: A ship's desired direction and path of travel, not to be confused with heading.

**Damage Control Locker**: Compartments throughout a ship or starbase which have pre-positioned repair materials for use by DC Teams.

**Damage Control Team**: A group of specially trained individuals charged with the responsibility to provide a quick-reaction repair response to damage incurred during combat operations. Each DC Team is responsible for a specific area of the ship or starbase and operates out of a Damage Control Locker.

**Damage Control Central**: Exercises primary control over all damage control activities throughout a ship or starbase. Staffed by specially trained personnel and located in the primary hull.

**Damage Control Secondary**: Exercises secondary control over all damage control activities throughout a ship or starbase in support or (if necessary) as a replacement for DC Central. Staffed by specially trained personnel and located in the secondary hull of a ship.

**DC Central**: See Damage Control Central.

**DC Secondary**: See Damage Control Secondary.

**DC Team**: See Damage Control Team.

**Dead Ahead**: Directly ahead of a ship: Bearing 000 Mark 0.

**Dead in the Water**: Said of an underway ship that is making neither headway nor sternway, a hold-over expression from nautical ships.

**Deck**: Horizontal partition in a ship (floor).

**Department**: Personnel assigned to a starship or starbase are segregated into sub-organizations composed of crewmembers who have similar duties. For example, all personnel who operate and maintain the propulsion units are assigned to Engineering Department.

**Department Head**: The senior officer assigned to a department aboard a ship or a starbase. This individual is charged with ensuring the personnel assigned to that specific department execute their duties in an efficient and effective manner.

**Derelict**: Abandoned vessel.

**Displacement**: The volume of space, expressed in metric tons, which a starship or starbase occupies. It is one facet of describing the physical parameters of a vessel. The term originally referred to the amount of fluid displaced by a vessel operating in a water environment but has been adapted to star ships.

**Division**: Within a department, specialists who are assigned responsibility for a specific area are divided into divisions. For example in the Engineering Department, those specialists who operate and maintain the offensive and defensive weapons systems of the ship are in the Weapons Systems Division of the Engineering Department.

**Division Officer**: The senior officer assigned to a division within a department aboard ship or starbase. This individual reports directly to the Department Head and is responsible for ensuring the personnel assigned to that specific division execute their duties in an efficient and effective manner.

**Dock**: Any structure which serves as a mooring point for a vessel; the act of so mooring.

**Draft**: The extreme height of a vessel.

**Drift**: The deviation of a ship from its plotted course or position.

**Drydock**: A dock which is equipped to refit or rebuild ships.

**ECHO** (**E**nhanced **C**ollimination via **H**armonic **O**scillation): An enhancement to the main offensive weapons of certain starships which increases the destructive force delivered to the target. Activation of this ECHO system must not be effected when the phaser bank is set on "stun," since it is lethal to all known life forms inhabiting the target area.

**Embark**: To go on board a ship preparatory to sailing.

**End on**: Head-to-head or stem-to-stem.

**Engineering Officer of the Watch**: The senior Engineer during each of the three duty shifts on a starship or starbase. This individual assumes all duties and responsibilities of the Chief Engineer while on watch.

**EOOW**: See Engineering Officer of the Watch.

**Eugene's Limit**: The theoretical upper limit of faster-than-light travel. At Eugene's Limit, the power requirement to maintain a warp field approaches infinity, and is, therefore, unattainable.

**Fantail**: The after end of a Hangar Deck on a starship or starbase.

**First Fleet**: A numbered fleet under Starfleet Command responsible for a specific sector (Quadrant 1) of Federation territory. Various ships and personnel are assigned to First Fleet in order to carry out this mission.

**First Officer**: Second-in-command aboard a commissioned Starfleet vessel. In the absence or incapacitation of the Commanding Officer, assumes all responsibilities and authority vested in that position. The equivalent officer on a starbase is called an Executive Officer.

**Flag Officer**: An officer above the rank of Captain, so called because he/she is entitled to fly his/her personal flag which, by stars, indicates rank.

**Flash Team**: A team put together by a responsible officer composed of individuals possessing specialized knowledge, abilities, or characteristics. Organized for a specific purpose, a Flash Team has limited existence and is disbanded after the particular task has been accomplished.

**Flat**: Grating or partial deck to provide walking and working surfaces, used extensively in engineering spaces.

**Fleet**: An organization of ships and structures (such as starbases and/or drydocks), all under one command.

**Forward**: Toward the bow; opposite of aft.

**Fourth Fleet**: A numbered fleet under Starfleet Command responsible for a specific sector (Quadrant 4) of Federation territory. Various ships and personnel are assigned to Fourth Fleet in order to carry out this mission.

**Frame**: The secondary structural members of a ship's hull.

**Hangar**: Space used for landing, launching, and parking shuttlecraft and auxiliary craft.

**Hard Over**: Extreme turn to one side.

**Hatch**: Removable cover to a gangway.

**Head**: Compartment containing sanitary facilities.

**Heading**: The direction a ship is facing while underway.

**Headway**: Forward motion of a ship.

**Hold**: Large cargo space aboard a ship.

**Home Fleet**: An unnumbered fleet under Starfleet Command responsible for a specific sector (Quadrant 0) of Federation territory. Various ships and personnel are assigned to the Home Fleet in order to carry out this mission.

**Impulse Drive**: Secondary means of propulsion for Starfleet vessels. It is utilized for sub-light travel in close proximity to planets and other bodies. Maximum speed which can be attained in impulse drive is less than the speed of light.

**Inboard**: Toward the centerline.

**Jury Rig**: Any makeshift device or repair.

**Keel**: The main strength members of a ship, upon which the frames and hull plates depend.

**Keelhaul**: To reprimand severely.

**Knock Off**: To cease what is being done; to stop work.

**Launch**: To maneuver a vessel from a dock, hangar bay, or planet surface.

**Lie To**: Said of a vessel when underway with no way on.

**Log**: Official record in which data or events that occurred during a watch are stored; a personal log is a record made by an individual ancillary to an official log.

**Mega-phaser**: An improved version of the standard phaser emplacements utilized as the main weapon system of some starships. It produces a larger destructive force than standard phasers and is often called a "cannon."

**Memory Alpha**: A planetoid set up by the Federation as a central library containing the total cultural history and scientific knowledge of all Federation members.

**MEMT**: See Mobile Emergency Medical Team.

**Mobile Emergency Medical Team**: Composed of a physician, a nurse, and other medically trained personnel; assigned to various locations throughout a ship or starbase during Red Alerts to respond to medical emergencies within a specified area of responsibility.

**Moor**: To anchor or make fast to a dock.

**Motto**: A word, phrase, or sentence chosen as expressive of the goals or ideals of an organization or individual. Most vessels and starbases in Starfleet have a motto.

**Nadir**: Directly below: Bearing 000 Mark –90.

**Neutral Zones**: Zones in space set up by treaties in which neither belligerent has control or is allowed to enter. In many cases, violation of a Neutral Zone is paramount to declaring war.

**Officer-of-the-Deck**: The senior officer of the watch on the Main Bridge of a starship. This officer has full responsibility for the safe operation, course, defense, and any other matter delegated by the Commanding Officer in the absence of the Commanding Officer or First Officer from the Main Bridge.

**Ordnance**: General term meaning weapons systems.

**Outboard**: Away from the centerline; toward the side of the vessel, or outside the vessel entirely.

**Overhaul**: To overtake another ship on the same heading; to undertake extensive repairs or modifications to a ship or facility.

**Overhead**: On a ship, equivalent to the ceiling of a building ashore; ships have overheads rather than ceilings.

**Padd** (Portable Archival Digital Device): A data storage device used by personnel to record information when the more powerful tricorder is inappropriate; i.e., personal logs. Both vocal and stylus input are available. Data transfer between the Main Library Computer and individual padds can be effected. There are five models of padds, classified by memory capacity: Model 1 (1GB), Model 2 (2GB), Model 3 (3GB), Model 4 (4GB) and Model 5 (5GB).

**Parsec** (**Par**allax of one **sec**ond of arc): A measure of distance in deep space, a parsec is equivalent to 3.261633 light years or 3.085678 x $10^{13}$ kilometers.

**Passageway**: Corridor or hallway on a ship.

**Pass the Word**: To repeat an order or information to all hands.

**Phaser** (**PHAS**ed **E**nergy **R**ectification): The main energy weapon of Starfleet starships; the main personal weapon utilized for offense and defense by individuals in Starfleet. They are usually issued for Landing Party use in an unknown situation or when circumstances dictate.

**Photon Torpedo**: First developed by the Romulans, these projectiles with a matter/anti-matter warhead deliver a more concentrated and destructive payload on a target than ship's phasers.

**Pipe Down**: An order to keep silent.

**Pipe the Side**: Ceremony in which sideboys are drawn up and the boatswain's pipe is blown when a high-ranking officer or distinguished visitor comes aboard.

**Pitch**: Rotation of a ship on the Y axis.

**Plank Owner**: A person who served aboard a ship or starbase at its commissioning.

**Port**: To the left of the centerline when facing forward, Bearing 270 Mark 0; a major spaceship landing field or orbital station.

**Primary Hull**: The "main hull" of a starship, where the majority of tactical and strategic control compartments are located. In Starfleet, the predominate shape of this primary hull is a disk, or saucer. In emergencies, it can be detached from the secondary hull and, using the impulse drive units, travel at limited speeds, landing on a planet's surface to provide living accommodations for the crew until assistance arrives. Once landed, the primary hull can be retrieved only by specialized equipment found in shipbuilding or conversion facilities.

**Prime Directive**: Starfleet General Order Number 1. Directs all Starfleet personnel to obey a policy of non-interference in the affairs of any culture. It is the guiding principle in relationships between Federation and non-Federation races.

**Quarters**: Living spaces aboard ship.

**Range**: Distance between observer and object.

**Red Alert**: Also called Battle Stations or General Quarters. The most extreme level of readiness for a ship in response to imminent danger on the ship, in the immediate vicinity, or possible offensive or defense action which might result in personnel casualties or damage to the ship.

**Relieve**: To take the place (duties) of another.

**Restricted Maneuverability Zone (RMZ)**: The use of warp drive within a planetary system causes an interaction between the ship's warp field envelope and the star's hydrostatic equilibrium. This, in turn, impacts on the star's Rayleigh Scattering Ratio. As a result, ships are restricted to the use of impulse power within the system's RMZ. This RMZ is different for each star system and is determined by the star's class, number of planets within the system and their relative positions, and other, more technical measurements.

**Rig**: To set up any piece of equipment.

**Roll**: Rotation of a ship on the X axis.

**Running Lights**: Navigational lights mounted on a ship's exterior; red for port, green for starboard, white at other, specific points; the standard flashing rate for running lights is 1.1 seconds.

**Scuttle**: A round, air-tight hatch; to self-destruct a vessel.

**Secondary Hull**: The second hull of a Starfleet starship in which the majority of the Engineering spaces and Warp Drive propulsion units are located. A Hangar Bay, cargo bays, and storage facilities are also usually located in the secondary hull.

**Second Fleet**: A numbered fleet under Starfleet Command responsible for a specific sector (Quadrant 2) of Federation territory. Various ships and personnel are assigned to Second Fleet in order to carry out this mission.

**Secondary Sickbay**: An auxiliary medical facility located in the secondary hull to handle local casualties or non-critical patient overflow from Main Sickbay.

**Sensor**: General term for a device which gathers data either in a passive or active mode.

**Shakedown**: The training of a new crew; the trial run of a prototype, or a vessel having finished refit.

**Shipshape**: Neat; clean; taut.

**Ship's (Starbase's) Manning Document**: A document which lists each position aboard a ship or starbase by the Billet Sequence Code along with the authorized grade for each and the name and rank of the individual filling that position.

**Ship's (Starbase's) Organization and Regulations Manual** (SORM): The document which details the organization of a ship or starbase and outlines the regulations to be followed while a member of the crew.

**Sickbay**: Ship or starbase's medical spaces and facilities.

**Side Boy**: Member of the honor guard welcoming VIPs.

**Skylark**: To engage in irresponsible behavior.

**SMD**: See Ship's Manning Document.

**SORM**: See Ship's Organization and Regulations Manual.

**Spline**: Straight, curved, or crooked line representing a ship's course in three-dimensions on a chart.

**Squadron**: A fighting unit composed of up to 20 vessels having a common mission or capabilities.

**Stanchions**: Girders used to support bulkheads, attached to frames.

**Stand By**: Prepare for.

**Starboard**: To the right of centerline when facing forward, Bearing 090 Mark 0.

**Stateroom**: A living compartment for an officer or passenger.

**Station**: A crew member's place of duty; position of a ship in a formation.

**Stern**: The aftermost part of a ship.

**Stow**: To pack articles of cargo in a space or container.

**Supercargo**: A individual who is physically on a ship but who is not part of the ship's company; a passenger. The term is usually reserved for members of Starfleet who are being transported on the ship, but it can be applied to any individual.

**Task Force**: Temporary grouping of units under one commander; formed for the purpose of carrying out a specific operation or mission.

**Thermocoat**: A non-reflective, non-refractive coating applied to the outer hull of Starfleet vessels under 90,000 metric tons displacement. Designed to aid the ship in evading detection by other sensor systems; application of this covering becomes cost- and weight-prohibitive, as well as ineffective, for large vessels.

**Third Fleet**: A numbered fleet under Starfleet Command responsible for a specific sector (Quadrant 3) of Federation territory. Various ships and personnel are assigned to Third Fleet in order to carry out this mission.

**Tractor Beam**: A repulsor/attractor device on starships and starbases which can manipulate large objects at a distance by altering their inertia as desired.

**Traverse Frame**: Structural member which extends outward from the centerline of a vessel.

**Turn In**: Retire to quarters; return articles to storage; report an individual for violation of a rule or regulation.

**Turn Out**: Get out of bed; order out a work party.

**Turn To**: Start work.

**Underway**: A ship is underway when not moored or in planetary orbit. She need not be actually moving; she is underway so long as she lies free in space and under her own power.

**Veer**: To swerve suddenly from a previous heading.

**Void**: An empty compartment or container; deep space.

**Warp Drive**: The main method of propulsion for Starfleet vessels which uses an intricate mix of matter and antimatter to attain speeds in excess of *c*. Warp drive is utilized for travel only outside of star systems because of the effect the drive can have on planets (see Restricted Maneuverability Zone).

**Warp Factor**: A measurement of speed in faster-than-light travel using the Warp Drive.

**Watch**: One of the three eight-hour periods into which a day is divided on board ships and some starbases; watches are denoted by the terms ALPHA, BETA and GAMMA.

**Wormhole**: An anomaly in space created by any one of several unique combinations of circumstances. A ship caught by a wormhole is seldom able to escape its effects.

**Yaw**: Rotation of a ship on the Z axis.

**Yellow Alert**: A condition of heightened readiness to respond to potentially dangerous situations either on the ship or in the immediate vicinity.

**Zenith**: Directly above, Bearing 000 Mark +90

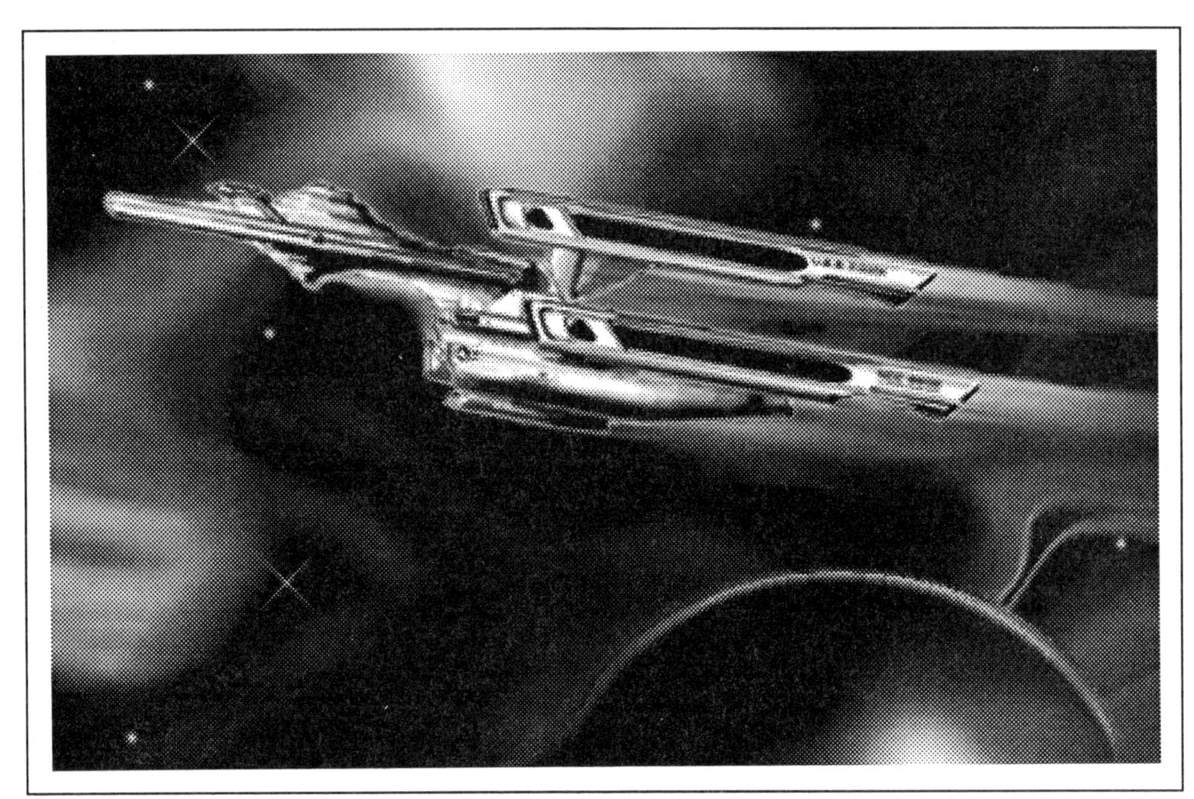

USS ZAHN (NCC-8606)

# INDEX